It's Not Worth The Weight

It's Not Worth The Weight

A 90-Day Weight Loss Devotional

Marlene Jenkins Cooper

Songs of Judah
Publishing, LLC

It's Not Worth the Weight / Marlene Jenkins Cooper — 1st edition.

Publisher: Songs of Judah Publishing, LLC

ISBN:978-0-9965817-1-4

1. Christian Weight Loss Devotional 2. Daily Devotional Women

3. Getting Healthy through Christ 4. Bible-Based Weight Loss

5. Christian Diet Books;

First Edition

Printed in the United States of America

To all of my family and friends,

Thanks to all of you who walked with me in the park or on the track, encouraged me, and worked alongside me while on my journey to living a healthy lifestyle.

Acknowledgments

First and foremost, I would like to thank God for helping me write this devotional and lose the unnecessary weight. As I chose this healthy lifestyle, I asked God for His help during the journey and asked Him for guidance on which scriptures would bless others and me as I wrote this devotional. I could never have done this project without the faith I have in God.

I would like to express my gratitude to all the people who had kind words of encouragement (and not-so-kind words, but those words helped too). To my all friends who were or who are still on this weight loss and healthy eating journey with me, I want to say how grateful I am for your support and comradeship. Thanks again to everyone who has encouraged me on this weight loss journey.

Above all, I want to thank my children, Joy and Mark, who encouraged me to get healthy and lose the unnecessary fat and weight. I've been on a weight loss journey their entire lives. They supported and encouraged me. Many thanks to my mom, dad, and siblings, who also encouraged me with their support. Thanks everyone!

Table of Contents

Introduction   xv

It's Not Worth The Weight!   1
YES, I CAN   2
Day 1

OUR TEMPLE   4
Day 2

WRITE IT DOWN   6
Day 3

WALK WITH JESUS   8
Day 4

RENEWING YOUR MIND   10
Day 5

ABIDE IN ME   12
Day 6

CHANGED BODIES   14
Day 7

PROSPER IN HEALTH   16
Day 8

DISCIPLINE   18
Day 9

THE GOALS   20
Day 10

TEMPTATIONS ARISE   22
Day 11

DROP THE BURDENS   24
Day 12

BE STRONG IN THE LORD   26
Day 13

HALLELUJAH!   28
Day 14

WHY?   30
Day 15

REST IN THE LORD   32
Day 16

MORE THAN A CONQUEROR   34
Day 17

KNOW YOUR NUMBERS!   36
Day 18

WHAT IS YOUR NAME?   38
Day 19

LIFT UP YOUR HANDS   40
Day 20

SALT THE EARTH   42
Day 21

CAST YOUR CARES   44
Day 22

A TRANSFORMATION   46
Day 23

ONE DAY AT A TIME   48
Day 24

WEARY?   50
Day 25

THE LUST OF THE EYE   52
Day 26

FOLLOW THE PLAN   54
Day 27

THE FUTURE ME   56
Day 28

FUEL FOR THE BODY   58
Day 29

DON'T GET WEARY!   60
Day 30

PRAYER and FASTING   62
Day 31

CONSISTENCY IS KEY   64
Day 32

EAT THE FRUIT   66
Day 33

FREEDOM IN CHRIST   68
Day 34

MY HELP!   70
Day 35

THE JOY THIEF   72
Day 36

THE FLESH SPEAKS 74
Day 37

THIS DAY 76
Day 38

CONFIDENCE IN HIM 78
Day 39

TEMPTATION 2.0 80
Day 40

OUR REFUGE and STRENGTH 82
Day 41

COVET NOT! 84
Day 42

LOVE, LOVE, L-O-V-E 86
Day 43

GOD'S MASTERPIECE 88
Day 44

LIVING WATER 90
Day 45

MY COMMITMENT 92
Day 46

ENCOURAGE YOURSELF 94
Day 47

THE BLOOD 96
Day 48

WHEN I AM WEAK 98
Day 49

LACK WISDOM? 100
Day 50

HEALS ALL MY DISEASES 102
Day 51

IN THE MORNING 104
Day 52

THE REQUIREMENT 106
Day 53

SELF-LOVE 108
Day 54

FRIENDS ON THE JOURNEY 110
Day 55

IS THIS FOOD FOR ME? 112
Day 56

NEW MERCIES ARE MINE   114
Day 57

ALL THINGS POSSIBLE   116
Day 58

HUMBLE ME   118
Day 59

VICTORY IS MINE   120
Day 60

WITHOUT MURMURINGS and
COMPLAINING   122
Day 61

MY NEW BODY   124
Day 62

THE FOOD TEST   126
Day 63

THAT'S LOVE   128
Day 64

IS LIFE MORE THAN FOOD?   130
Day 65

THE DESIRES OF THE FLESH   132
DAY 66

I SEE YOU   134
Day 67

A TESTIMONY   136
Day 68

I WILL RESTORE   138
Day 69

DISCOURAGED?   140
Day 70

MY HOPE   142
Day 71

MY WORDS HAVE POWER   144
Day 72

IS ANYTHING TOO HARD?   146
Day 73

GOD, THE SUPPLIER   148
Day 74

JESUS, THE CHEF   150
Day 75

HAVING THE MIND OF CHRIST   152
Day 76

SATISFY HIM   154
Day 77

SELF-CONTROL IN ALL THINGS   156
Day 78

GIVE THANKS   158
Day 79

TEMPTATION 3.0   160
Day 80

HOPE IN THE LORD   162
Day 81

THE PLAN   164
Day 82

THE JOURNEY   166
Day 83

PERFECT PEACE   168
Day 84

LACK CONFIDENCE?   170
Day 85

THE TRUTH   172
Day 86

WHATSOEVER YE DO   174
Day 87

REJOICE IN THE DANCE   176
Day 88

A JOYFUL HEART   178
Day 89

RECOMMIT   180
Day 90

Marlene's Weight Loss Food Plan   183
Healthy Lifestyle Tips Index   186
Sample Mealtime Prayers   191
Invitation to Salvation   192
Repentant Sinner's Prayer for Salvation   195
ABOUT THE AUTHOR   197
DEVOTIONAL THEME INDEX   199
DEVOTIONAL SCRIPTURE INDEX   203
ENDNOTES   209

AFTERWORD   211
FEEDBACK and SUPPORT   212

Also by Marlene Jenkins Cooper   213

Introduction

It's Not Worth the Weight originated out of my need for such a book to encourage and assist me in the middle of my weight loss/healthy eating journey. I desired short devotionals to share with my friends and myself, guiding us on our weight loss journey with God's help. I connected each devotional to a scripture, a reflection, a prayer, and a healthy lifestyle tip. Despite having read many articles and books on diets, weight loss, healthy eating, and food plans, there was a divine calling placed on my heart by the Lord. He inspired me to write a 90-day devotional to encourage myself and others on a journey toward healthier eating.

During a prayer session with a ministry group, I'll never forget asking a group of believers to pray for my overeating issues. One sister in Christ just laughed when she heard my prayer request. Perhaps this prayer request is only given in a weight loss prayer group or food addiction support group. At a prayer service, I was in line for a special prayer with a prayer warrior. When it was my turn for prayer, the gentleman asked for my prayer request so he could specifically pray for me. He was stunned and taken aback when he heard my prayer request. The man didn't laugh but prayed for me. Yes, Lord!

The God of my salvation helped me control my eating habits, choose smaller portions, and believe I could win at weight loss with a healthy eating food plan.

May your weight loss journey be uplifted through your dedication to healthy eating, engaging with the devotionals, and reading the scriptures. Let's walk with God and make conscious choices in our diet for a rewarding path ahead!

The purpose of *It's Not Worth the Weight* is to give the reader encouragement on their weight loss/healthy eating journey as they read scripture, reflect, pray, and learn tips and strategies for healthy eating. *It's Not Worth the Weight* will foster time alone with God during personal devotions. My prayer is that your healthy eating journey and personal devotions will enrich your weight loss experience through the time spent together in the Word of God. So, prioritize eating right and walking with God!

Each of the ninety devotionals requires about five minutes before or after a meal or at another designated time. Each devotional begins with scripture, then offers a reflection and a brief prayer, and closes with a healthy tip.

Also, write additional thoughts or comments in a journal or in the margins that will record your thoughts and feelings on a particular day.

As you embark on this journey with *It's Not Worth The Weight*, may you find strength and inspiration in the scriptures and devotionals. God bless your path as you step towards a healthier and happy you!

It's Not Worth The Weight!

A 90-DAY WEIGHT LOSS DEVOTIONAL

YES, I CAN

Day 1

Philippians 4:13 (NIV)
I can do all this through him who gives me strength.

I can do all things! Yes, we can, but not on our own strength. We need the strength and power of Jesus to complete all things. We can draw strength from the Lord. Choose a healthier lifestyle and be consistent every day! There may be people out there whose bodies do not crave or want flour, sugar, large portions, carbohydrates, cakes, and candy, but my body wants it all and in large quantities.

Our bodies want what they want! In the United States of America, over two-thirds of Americans are overweight or obese.[1] Are we in that number? We must change our eating habits.

There is help for those struggling today. Many eat too many calories, saturated fat, refined sugar, and bleached flour. Jesus is concerned about our health and our wanting to take care of the temple He has given us. Ask for help. Rely on God's power to help in eliminating food items that will increase fat and weight in your body. Two people can eat the same thing, gaining more than the other. Our bodies and their metabolisms react to food differently.

Well, there are several reasons for this. No matter what, we want to live in a healthy body so we can do our daily tasks each day and minister to the body of Christ. How can we help others if our bodies are all broken down with weight-related diseases?

It is difficult to do the steps of eating healthy, but God wants to help us. He will partner with us and assist us on the journey. There have been times when I want to overeat. I hear Philippians 4:13, *I can do all things through Christ that strengtheneth me.* Now, when He gives us strength to resist eating an additional 500 calories in a day, do not refuse His help. Take His help and resist the urge to overeat. I can eat healthily. Why? Because God gives me strength and power if I tap into His might. Yes, I can, with the Lord's help.

Dear Lord,

I am ever so grateful for the strength which you give me. Thank you for helping me on my weight loss journey. When temptations arise, please remind me I can do all things through Christ that strengthens me. Thank you, dear Lord.

In Jesus' name,
Amen

Healthy Lifestyle Tip – Use portion control for each food group on your plate.

OUR TEMPLE
Day 2

I Corinthians 3:16-17
Know not that ye are the temple of God, and that the Spirit of God dwelleth in you? *[17]* *If any man defile the temple of God, him shall God destroy; for the temple of God is holy, which temple ye are.*

Our temple is the body we live in. Each of us receives one body at birth. Since our bodies are gifts from God, it is our duty to take care of our temples. Our bodies react to what we feed them. Our bodies calculate what we have put in them and then choose to store the fat or burn it up.

Let's take care of the body that was given to us at birth. Fueling our bodies with food is important. Yes, of course, God wants us to eat. However, constantly fueling our bodies with foods that are not good for us will harm many of us. Let's choose to eat those foods that are healthy for us and occasionally partake of other foods.

There is no time like the present to eat right, move and exercise, and watch our portion control. Yes, Jesus died on the cross for us. Yes,

4

we will have changed bodies when Jesus returns. However, it is our duty to take care of what God has given us. This includes our body, health, money, property, offspring (children), and our minds.

The next time a food choice situation arises, ask yourself, Will this food aid in my weight loss or do my body good? Will this food store fat calories from consumption in my body? How long will the excess calories, which turned into fat from this food, stay in my body? How long do I want a broken-down body? Sometimes our bodies do not rebel until it's too late. Then we pray to God, please heal me. With that said, let's choose to eat and live a healthy lifestyle. Your body will thank you.

Is it possible to go back to our old eating habits? Yes, and if we go back to our old bad eating habits, the weight will come back. Those shrunken fat cells want to be re-energized. The re-energized fat cells that were shrunken from weight loss will swell again. Take care of the temple! Stay on the journey of healthy eating.

Please Lord,

Lead me day by day as I eat those healthy foods that fuel my body!
Help me make good food choices.
In Jesus' name,

Amen

Healthy Lifestyle Tip - Let sleeping and shrunken fat cells stay shrunken. Do not re-energize them with excess calories.

WRITE IT DOWN

Day 3

Habakkuk 2:2 ESV
And the LORD answered me: Write the vision; make it plain on tablets,
so he may run who reads it.

What is the plan? Name the prescribed weight loss plan that will enable the weight to come off. When are your planned exercise/workout days and times? Is there a food plan for each day comprising the three mealtimes or six small meals? Identify the bad eating habits that need to be replaced with good eating habits. Writing the plan will give you clarity and direction.

When the prophet Habakkuk in the Old Testament had a problem and needed help from the Lord, the Lord told him to write the vision on a tablet and make it plain and clear. Excess weight, overweight, and obesity are major problems. These problems are not the same as the prophet Habakkuk was experiencing, but they are still problems that concern us. God cares about everything that concerns us (Psalm 138:8).

Although losing weight may not be a simple journey, let the Lord walk alongside you during the process. There are many weight loss plans, diets, and healthy lifestyle tips and strategies, but choose the ones that work with your body and lifestyle. Consistently work on the plan each day and every meal.

Consider journaling your thoughts about this weight loss/healthy eating journey. In a journal or notebook, write about your feelings when you emotionally eat or choose the wrong food or food portions. Write about the joy experienced when excess weight leaves the body or the feelings of elation when you make great healthy decisions for your body. What feelings or emotions do you experience during or after the workout or exercise? As I reread my weight loss journals, it's uplifting to see how I progressed and even read about my setbacks. My weight loss journey is a journey documented by my thoughts and feelings, food menus, and data from exercise and weigh-ins.

What's the plan? Write it down and make it plain. Plan ahead.

Dear Lord,

Just a closer walk with Thee makes it right. My prayer is to let the scriptures speak to me as I walk with you on this weight loss journey. When I stray, please lead me back to making the right choices about my food.
In Jesus' name,
Amen

Healthy Lifestyle Tip – Write your food plan in a food journal and, possibly, privately post the plan somewhere in your home. Make the plan clear. Then consistently follow the plan.

WALK WITH JESUS

Day 4

Matthew 6:33
But seek ye first the kingdom of God, and his righteousness; and all
these things shall be added unto you.

Following a weight loss program, choosing to live a healthier lifestyle, or simply making a few changes in one's diet can be overwhelming for some. Asking Jesus for His help while on this journey will give us the support needed to walk this path. Seek God's help, direction, and approval on all things.

Walk with Jesus, hold His hand, and don't stray from His path. Jesus will lead us in the right direction with our eating habits, food plans, and exercise regime, and help us stay the course. Seek His guidance for healthy weight loss.

Walking is an excellent form of exercise. However, select an exercise routine you can engage in 4-6 times per week. There is research that states one should exercise in the morning so that the body burns calories all day.[1] Also, get up early to pray and hear the voice of God. (Psalm 5:3)

As we physically walk, it is necessary to move our feet and be directional in our steps. Head up and look ahead! As we walk our Christian journey, we want the Lord to direct our spiritual steps and guide our lives. Look up and see God. The Lord will help us as we walk on different terrains (trials, tribulations, and happiness), and He will hold our hand and guide us. Jesus is always with us. He never leaves or forsakes us.

The next time a situation arises that seems too difficult to bear, know that your Heavenly Father is walking alongside you. Trust Him as you walk with Him. Let Him lead and guide you. He is rooting for you!

Dear Lord,

I thank you for your guidance as you walk with me. Thanks for holding my hand as you guide me through life's journeys, especially through living a healthy lifestyle.
In the precious name of Jesus,

Amen

Healthy Lifestyle Tip - Walk for at least 30 minutes a day for at least 5 days a week. (If you are a beginner, gradually build up to 30 minutes a day.)

RENEWING YOUR MIND

Day 5

Ephesians 4:23
And be renewed in the spirit of your mind;

Our mind controls our thoughts and choices. Many times, we say inappropriate things to ourselves. We say things such as, "I'll never lose this weight." Well, if you tell yourself those negative things, I guess the excess weight will not leave. Another statement, "I'll just die fat!" I've said this before. God does not honor those words.

We must transform our minds and words. Change the negative thoughts and words about our ourselves and bodies. Replace negative thoughts with positive ones. It's a proven fact that eating healthy results in significant benefits. If you subscribe to a weight loss program that works for your body, your body will respond by dropping fat. We must do the work!

Philippians 4:8 declares, *Finally, brethren, whatsoever things are true, whatsoever things are honest, whatsoever things are just, whatsoever things are pure, whatsoever things are lovely, whatsoever things are of good report; if there be any virtue, and if there be any praise, think on these things.* Calling ourselves negative names is not uplifting, and those names are not how God sees us. Pray and ask God to transform your mind. Consistently read the Word of God. Focus on Him!

As you transform your mind and words with God's Word, you can transform the body as well while changing to healthy eating habits. What a transformation! *Let this mind be in you, which was also in Christ Jesus!* (Philippians 2:5) Get your mind right! Change those negative thoughts about food and exercise.

See the good in changing your ways and words. Watch, feel, and see what happens. Less of you will be the result.

Dear Lord,

A transformation of my mind and body is my desire, I pray. I offer praise and thanks to you on this day.
In Jesus' name,

Amen

Healthy Lifestyle Tip – Replace unhealthy eating habits and thoughts with healthy ones. List them.

ABIDE IN ME

Day 6

John 15:5 (NKJV)
I am the vine, you are the branches. He who abides in Me, and I in
him, bears much fruit; for without Me you can do nothing.

"Abide with Me!" is a wonderful hymn based on the above scripture. Abide in Jesus. Jesus makes this statement in the book of John. The vine feeds and gives nutrition to the branches. We are the branches and Jesus is the vine. Get your strength from the Lord, which will enable you to continue your weight loss/healthy eating journey with significant results. Abide in Jesus. This journey can be difficult, but by abiding in Him, making changes towards healthy living will cause victorious weight loss that will result in better health. These changes can be small.

This great opportunity to change our ways of reconstructing a body that will glorify God is awesome. Knowing that exercise, changing our food portions, having a food plan, changing our minds and bad eating habits, and reducing sugar intake can rid some risks of weight-related diseases and give us hope. Unfortunately, we cannot just pray away obesity or excess weight on our bodies. We must have a plan. We are managers of the bodies God gave us. Chose to be a good steward of the body God gave us. Get that body into shape! Let our bodies and lives match the Word of God. Without God, I can do nothing.

Dear Lord,

I offer myself to you. I want to honor you through my body and lifestyle. You are worthy of my actions towards the body you have entrusted to me. May my lifestyle changes lead me to live a healthier life. Let my body edify and glorify you, O Lord.
In the precious name of Jesus,

Amen

Healthy Tip – Reduce at least 5-15 percent of excess weight. For most people, reducing just 5-15 percent of one's excess body weight will improve the health of their bodies.[1]

CHANGED BODIES

Day 7

Philippians 3:20-21 (NIV)
But our citizenship is in heaven. And we eagerly await a Savior from there, the Lord Jesus Christ, ²¹who, by the power that enables him to bring everything under his control, will transform our lowly bodies so that they will be like his glorious body.

When Jesus comes for His church at His second coming, we will transcend into heaven, and Jesus will transform our bodies into bodies without flaws. (I Corinthians 15:51-53) We do not know the hour or day when this will occur. We are anxiously waiting for that day. But until then, what about the bodies we are living in now? While we are here on earth, why not physically change our bodies for the betterment of our health? Does the pain in our joints, difficulty in walking and exercising, and possibly experiencing weight-related health diseases make for easy living?

As we make small changes to our diet, our bodies will respond

14

and slowly change. This will not happen overnight; we did not gain excess weight overnight. Trust the process, show up every day for you, and later, see less of you.

What a beautiful experience to feel healthy, see lower numbers on the scale, or feel the difference in the fit of our clothes. These changes in our bodies are a testament to embracing a fresh, health-conscious way of life or committing to a weight loss regimen. Although these changes will not happen overnight, with discipline and a plan, weight loss is achievable. Hallelujah. All glory to God.

When we change our bodies through diet and exercise, we may still have some flaws. However, hopefully, we are living a better quality of life. Let's take action now. Rather than awaiting Jesus to change our bodies upon His return for His church, let's embrace the present and prioritize a healthy body that functions optimally. Until Jesus returns, let's live in a well-functioning, healthy body.

Dear Lord,

I am grateful that you will change our bodies when you come back for your church. We will have a changed body without diseases or ailments. As I live and eat differently, please help me make the changes that I can make for a healthier body and lifestyle. Lord, I need your help. This is difficult. Thank you, Jesus, for praying for me.
In Jesus' name,

Amen

Healthy Lifestyle Tip – Eliminate or reduce the amount of refined sugar and processed carbohydrates.

PROSPER IN HEALTH

Day 8

III John 1:2 (ESV)
Beloved, I pray that all may go well with you and that you may be in
good health, as it goes well with your soul.

J ohn, the writer of our scripture reference, is speaking of prospering. First, even as thy soul prospers, which includes having a great relationship with our Lord and Savior. Then, prosper in all things, which includes health.

It is amazing how many people want to only prosper in monetary riches. Some people believe money rules the world. However, no amount of money can buy good health. Money can buy great healthcare, medicines, and excellent care, but money cannot buy good health. Let's be healthy and take care of the bodies God gave us!

How long has your journey of weight loss been? How many times have you started a diet and stopped? This time, continue on your journey all the way to the end. Reread your favorite devotionals in this book and speak the scriptures for encouragement. God is walking with us on this journey. God wants us to prosper and be in good health. We cannot go back to the old eating habits that led us to an unhealthy body or possibly diabetes, high blood pressure, high cholesterol, obesity, and the other diseases that can come with excess weight. Preventing and/or lowering the risk for those diseases keeps us thriving and alive.

Our bodies are the temple of the Holy Ghost. We are not our own, and we were bought with a price (I Corinthians 6:19-20) Thanks be to Jesus for His help, provisions, The Word of God, compassion, and forgiveness.

Dear Lord,

I am grateful for the body that was given to me at birth. I apologize for not taking care of my temple with my poor eating habits, lack of sleep, exercise, and portion control. Thanks for the opportunity to know where I have erred! Lord, I want to stay on the healthy eating journey. My desire is to prosper in my relationship with you and then in all things.
In the precious name of Jesus,

Amen

Healthy Lifestyle Tip – Live a daily life of consistent, healthy eating habits.

DISCIPLINE

Day 9

II Timothy 1:7 ESV
For God gave us a spirit not of fear but of power and love and self-control.

The apostle Paul writes to Timothy about not being fearful or timid. Paul further states that God gives us power, love, and self-control. Self-control means being able to control one's self. God will help us exercise self-control over our choices of food and food portions. Self-discipline is essential for a successful weight loss journey, but there is help! Since we eat every day, practicing self-restraint becomes a constant requirement. Ask the Savior to help you.

At a recent early morning "meetup" or gathering after a bike ride (I was a guest and didn't bike ride), there was fellowship with a barista, bagels, brownies, and home-baked chocolate chip cookies. Not a piece of fruit was in sight, except for the figs on the tree! A gentleman offered me a large chocolate chip cookie. I politely refused. (Nothing wrong with a chocolate cookie, but the cookie was not on my plan.) Honestly, I really wanted it. The gentleman said, "I respect your discipline." "Thank you, sir, for those kind words," I replied. I left the gathering with gratitude for myself; I did not indulge.

Do you fear failure to follow through on this healthy eating journey? How many diets have you attempted and not succeeded? When the fear of failure grips you and the lack of confidence engulfs you, hold on to God's Word in II Timothy 1:7 (ESV). We all need the confidence that we will continue this healthy lifestyle journey and be successful.

Choose to make wise choices. Some individuals gradually develop the ability to display discipline or self-control. This is my testimony. So glad that I could enjoy the time of fellowship with my cappuccino with almond milk. I left the event without indulging or consuming any bakery items. Be encouraged. We can become self-disciplined.

Thank you, Jesus! Self-discipline!

Dear Lord,

I choose to make healthy choices about my food. Making good daily decisions about my food will help my temple to thrive. Lead me, Lord, in that direction.
In Jesus' name,

Amen

Healthy Lifestyle Tip - Eat before attending an event. Consider taking a healthy snack or fruit.

THE GOALS

Day 10

Psalm 37:4 (ESV)
Delight yourself in the Lord, and he will give you the desires of your heart.

How do you envision yourself in 30, 60, or 90 days? What goals do you want to achieve? Is it shedding twenty pounds of excess fat from your body? Could it be eliminating stomach (visceral) fat around your stomach? Are we trying to move closer to a right-sized body? Is attaining a healthy weight, a normal BMI, and lowering your blood pressure our goals?

Define and write the goals! What is the plan and timeline to achieve the goals? Are the goals measurable and achievable in the designated timeframe? Consider using the S.M.A.R.T. goal method for achieving success with your goals. The acronym S.M.A.R.T. stands for Specific, Measurable, Achievable, Relevant, and Time-bound. Use these criteria to assist with attaining your goals. [1]

Each goal should be realistic, doable, and attainable. Establish a long-term goal and then break it down into short-term goals. List the steps on how the goals will be attainable. Give a time frame to reach the goals. Seek guidance and support from God.

For example,

Long Term Goal - 45-50 pounds in 6 months
Short-Term Goals
Goal - Lose 8 pounds in 30 days
How - Walk 5 days a week for 30 minutes
Plan meals at the start of the day
Avoid consuming sodas and candy
Drink 6-8 eight-ounce glasses of water a day

With discipline, determination, and prayer, these goals are achievable. Despite potential date variations, stay committed. Challenges may postpone progress, but persevere. Let struggles and challenges spur you on to the finish line. Call upon Him!

Dear Heavenly Father,

I give my goals to you. These goals are the desires of my heart. I want to live in a right-sized body that glorifies you. Please help me not to make poor decisions concerning eating foods that are not good for me and/or unhealthy portions that add excess weight.
In Jesus' name,
Amen

Healthy Lifestyle Tip – Set specific, measurable, achievable, relevant, and time-bound goals. Write them down.

TEMPTATIONS ARISE

Day 11

I Corinthians 10:13
There hath no temptation taken you but such as is common to man:
but God is faithful, who will not suffer you to be tempted above that ye
are able; but will with the temptation also make a way to escape, that
ye may be able to bear it.

Temptation is everywhere. We can see food advertisements on billboards while driving, television commercials, on social media, pop-ups on internet sites, magazine ads, and even the video screen above the gas pump console. Other sources of temptation include emotional triggers, social settings, easy food access, mindless eating, food aroma, and unhealthy habits are other sources that contribute to temptations. When food temptations or cravings arise, ask yourself two questions. Will partaking of this food add good nourishment to my body? Will this food or binge help me meet my goals? Decide. Answer the questions. The response is your choice.

Fitness trackers such as a Fitbit, Garmin watch, and/or Apple Watch will not make the choices for us. These devices motivate many people with the weight loss process, but the decision to eat and exercise is up to us. Temptations and unhealthy cravings will come. How will we handle them? Have a plan. Be prepared. The question is not if temptation will come, but when and how you will handle it.

Since temptations will arise, set yourself up for success. Discover effective ways to handle temptation. Do not go to the supermarket hungry. When dining out, review menus beforehand and choose your selections. Keep healthy snacks in the car. Carry a piece of your favorite fruit with you. Never leave the house on an empty stomach. How will you handle future temptations and cravings?

God will give us the strength that we need for the journey. While temptations may arise, look to the hills from where our help comes from. (Psalm 121:1-2) Rely on God's strength not to give in to temptation and those strong cravings! When we fall and give in to those cravings that do not help us, get back up, evaluate the fall, regroup, recommit, and continue the journey.

Dear Lord,

When temptation arises, I must choose to make the right choices for my body. Please help me Lord not to make poor decisions concerning eating foods that are not good for me and/or not on my food plan. I can do this, Lord. Thank you.
In Jesus' name,

Amen

Healthy Lifestyle Tip – Eliminate or reduce sugary drinks from your diet.

DROP THE BURDENS

Day 12

Psalm 55:22
Cast thy burden upon the LORD, and he shall sustain thee: he shall
never suffer the righteous to be moved.

Excess weight is a burden on our bodies. Let's drop the burden! It's a heavy load; heavy on our backs, legs, joints, arteries, organs, minds, and more. Carrying the extra weight is an extreme physical, emotional, and spiritual burden for many. For some, this burden has been for a long period, and for others, a brief season. (Did you experience weight gain during the Covid-19 Pandemic?) Excess weight is a burden that we don't have to carry. What is the plan for the eradication of excess weight? What are we doing to our bodies?

Cast your burdens upon the Lord. While exercising, walking, working around the house, or while sad, sing the songs of encouragement: "Cares Chorus," "Cast Your Burden unto Jesus," or

"Lay your burdens at the feet of Jesus." He cares for us! Give your burdens to the Lord.

Let the Word of God help you lose weight! Read, speak, recite, meditate, and post scriptures on the wall that will aid, encourage, inspire, and uplift you in losing the burden of weight on your body. How much weight have we released? How does the body feel and look? *I can do all things through Christ which strengthens me.* (Philippians 4:13)

While on this journey, take pictures of yourself. Record and document what the Lord has done and is doing in your life. The documentation will show the transformation of the excess weight leaving your body. Progress pictures will be a reminder of how consistent changes in healthy food-eating habits have lightened the load. Any other burdens that need to be unloaded? Remember to give all cares and burdens to the Lord. Keep going. Drop the burdens. For many of us, burdens are not just excess weight, but emotional weight, low self-esteem, lack of self-love, and debt, for example. Don't quit! You got this.

Dear Lord Jesus,

Touch me, Lord Jesus! Give me the mind, Lord, to be consistent with my healthy eating choices. Please heal my diseases. Please touch me, Lord, with your healing hands.
In Jesus' name,

Amen

Healthy Lifestyle tip: Place a scripture (use one from this devotional book) that encourages weight loss on the refrigerator or somewhere in the kitchen.

BE STRONG IN THE LORD
Day 13

Ephesians 6:10 (NIV)
Finally, be strong in the Lord and in his mighty power.

Be strong. These two words are simple but super powerful. Be strong in His might. Mighty is our God. He is strong and mighty. Walk, eat, prepare meals, and exercise in His might. That's a lot of power.

God will help us. His power is available to assist us on our weight loss/healthy eating journey. By His might and power. Yes, Lord!

Will there be mess-ups, failures, binges, or giving in to unhealthy cravings? Yes, those are significant possibilities. Guilt may try to overcome you. Do not let it cripple you or stall your journey. Rebuke the guilt! Forgive yourself and get back on track for the very next meal or the next morning. Minimize the damage (added weight). We cannot fool the body. The body continually calculates what foods it consumed, which includes every bite, lick, and taste that passes through our lips. Our bodies know. For some, it takes great willpower and strength to eat right. Since another meal is coming, choose to make healthy choices.

There are many examples in the Bible where men and women failed on other types of journeys. The Apostle Peter lied three times in a row, David the Psalmist killed a man, and Elijah got scared and ran from Jezebel. Each one recovered from their failures and did mightily for the Lord. So, forgive yourself when you are not strong when making great food choices. Decide to do better next time and move on. Rely on the Lord. Your strength is in the Lord.

Be strong and finish strong in His mighty power. You got this. Stay on track.

Dear Lord,

I speak of the mighty power of God that reigns within me. I move, live, and have my being in the power of God. God is my help and my strength! Food will not reign over me. There is none other. I will be strong in Your power.
In Jesus' name,

Amen

Healthy Lifestyle Tip – Enhance your lifestyle with small changes to achieve healthy living and potential weight loss.

HALLELUJAH!

Day 14

Revelation 19:1
And after these things I heard a great voice of much people in heaven,
saying, Alleluia; Salvation, and glory, and honour, and power, unto the
Lord our God.

Hallelujah means praise the Lord. David praised the Lord throughout many of the chapters in the book of Psalms. It is the only place the word hallelujah appears in the Old Testament. In the New Testament, hallelujah or alleluia only appears in the book of Revelation. Alleluia has also translated praise the Lord.

Praise the Lord for what He has done for me on my weight loss journey. Hallelujah, I lost 5 pounds. Hallelujah, I did not binge eat today. Praise the Lord, I made wise food choices. Hallelujah, I ate appropriate food portions.

At certain points, we may make poor decisions regarding our food choices and portions. The key lies in how we deal with such situations. No need to get depressed, sad, or despondent. Get back on your feet, dust off the setbacks, and recommit to making the right decisions for yourself. The devil would love for us to get defeated and stop our healthy lifestyle journey. Do not stop! Even when we mess up, praise the Lord, we have the mind to regroup and do better next time. Praise the Lord for small and large successes, which can mean not giving in to temptation, losing excess fat, and making good food choices.

Congratulate yourself with non-food-related rewards. i.e., a sticker placed in your journal, a massage, a new food scale, buying yourself flowers, buying a book, going to the beauty shop, purchasing new workout gear, or just patting yourself on the back.

The Lord is so worthy to be praised. Let all the people praise Thee, even when struggling on this weight loss journey. Hallelujah, give glory to God! Praise the Lord.

Dear Lord,

I give you praise today, my dear Father. Our words of hallelujah offer praises unto you for the steps that I am making in the right direction in my journey to eat in control. I give you praise for the mess-ups that may happen. I praise you for who you are and for your wondrous works. Lord, I thank you and praise you on this day.
In Jesus' name,

Amen

Healthy Lifestyle Tip – Praise the Lord for small and big wins. Celebrate with non-food rewards, big or small.

WHY?

Day 15

I Corinthians 6:19-20
What? know ye not that your body is the temple of the Holy Ghost
which is in you, which ye have of God, and ye are not your own? 20
For ye are bought with a price: therefore glorify God in your body and
in your spirit, which are God's.

Why am I on this journey? What is your "why" statement? Why do I want to lose weight or live a healthy lifestyle? Speak, write, and post your "why" statement on the wall, journal, or in notes on your phone! Write it down and make it plain to you.

How did I get here? Why do I weigh what I weigh? Everyone's answer will be different, but maybe similar. A healthy body needs a healthy diet for nutrition and good health. Consistent eating of chocolate cake and super-sized fast-food meals won't aid the body in great nutrition. Maintain a healthy diet for great health.

Why can't I quit this healthy living journey? List these reasons in your journal. The goal is to be in our right-sized healthy bodies. What are my realistic goals and benchmarks for this journey? Are they

30

written down? What benefits will I receive for knowing and doing my "Why?" Do you know them?

1. Increased mobility
2. More energy
3. Lower blood pressures
4. Lower A1c numbers
5. Quality sleep
6. Sleep apnea gone
7. Lower risks for weight-related diseases
8. (Your benefit.) - _____
9. (Your benefit.) - _____
10. (Your benefit.) - _____

Have you experienced any of the above benefits yet? Place a star or sticker and the date when you have experienced one or more of the above benefits.

Dear Lord,

You are strong and mighty. I walk in your power and might. Without you, I am helpless. I praise you, Lord God, for your mighty acts, wisdom, and strength. Let me remember and not forget my "why." I trust in you, my deliverer of all things.
In Jesus' name,
Amen

Healthy Lifestyle Tip – Make a poster (large or small) about the "Whys" of your weight loss journey.

REST IN THE LORD
Day 16

Matthew 11:28-30
Come unto me, all ye that labour and are heavy laden, and I will give
you rest. [29]Take my yoke upon you, and learn of me; for I am meek and
lowly in heart: and ye shall find rest unto your souls.[30] For my yoke is
easy, and my burden is light.

God rested on the seventh day of creation, and He called it the Sabbath. Our Heavenly Father wants us to physically and spiritually rest in Him. He wants to rejuvenate our bodies while we physically and spiritually rest.

Our bodies, our temples, need rest. The average person needs 7-9 hours of sleep a night. Our bodies need to renew, regenerate, and regroup. We cannot do this while watching movies and television, playing cards, and running errands. Weight gain or stalled weight loss can happen if we do not give proper sleep to the body.

During sleep, God renews our bodies. It is essential to get proper rest each night. What impact does inadequate sleep or staying awake for over 24 hours have on your body? Many of us do not perform at our best. God created our bodies to require rest.

Athletes must also rest their bodies from certain exercises because our muscles need time to recover. Some athletes rest 2-3 days a week or change their workout routine to a less strenuous one. Body rest elevates the possibility of injury because of over-training.

According to the weight of fish, meat, or poultry, the protein must rest after we have cooked it for a period before slicing and consumption. The resting period gives the juices in the meat/fish to relax and redistribute. (Free cooking tip.)

The words mentioned in today's devotional-rejuvenate, renew, regroup, rest, and recover—share a common theme. They all share the prefix "re," which means again. Each word conveys starting anew, restoring, and refreshing something that has been depleted or worn out.

In a spiritual sense, Jesus invites us to release our burdens to Him. Jesus said, "My burden is light." Lift your burdens upon the Lord, for He is the only one who can carry them all. Find rest in the Lord as you trust, obey, listen, depend, rely, and relax in His presence. Allow your body, both spiritually and physically, to find rest in Him! Rest in the Lord and experience His peace.

Dear Lord,

I am resting in you with my life, body, soul, and mind. Please prick my heart when I forget to trust, depend, obey, listen, and rest in you. As I sleep each night, help me give my body the proper rest it needs to rejuvenate and renew itself. May my sleep be peaceful as I rest in you.
In Jesus' name,
Amen

Healthy Lifestyle Tip – Strive for 7-9 hours of sleep each night.

MORE THAN A CONQUEROR
Day 17

Romans 8:37
Nay, in all these things we are more than conquerors through him that
loved us.

Losing weight, sticking to a food plan, exercising on a plan, and eating healthy/clean at all times for some of us is a major feat. For many, this is a way of life. The entire weight loss process is scientific. To lose weight, there must be a caloric deficit. Eat less, move more! This command is only four words, but the doing is often difficult. Stay the course, meal by meal and day by day.

But we are more than conquerors. With the strength that Jesus gives, the Bible says that we are more than conquerors. We can win! We can be successful with our eating habits, healthy lifestyle, and exercise regime, but rely on God to help. In Jesus' name, we are winners.

Our ultimate hope lies in Christ Jesus. We can be victorious.

There is hope that we can win by eating healthy. Look to Jesus, our blessed hope. With dieting, eating healthy, and eating on a food plan, it's common to feel discouraged or hopeless. Jesus will walk alongside us as we change our eating habits. With God's help, we can respect and care for our bodies.

Have you seen any progress in eating a healthy diet? How do you feel and look? Let's thank God for the weight we have shed - whether it be 3, 5, 25, 50, 75, or even 100 pounds. Are you complaining every time you eat healthily? Resist the urge to complain. Let's rejoice and give Him praise for the journey. Do not invite the return of excess weight through our old, poor eating habits.

Blessed to have hope, which is rooted and based in Christ Jesus. We will win. When situations in our lives look bleak, we are to look to Jesus, our blessed hope. We are more than a conqueror in Christ Jesus!

Dear Lord Jesus,

I will win at eating healthy because I am more than a conqueror. My trust, hope, dreams, and weight loss plans are in your hands. I can do this with your help. When I falter, please pick me up. You are my strength. I see you as you see me. Thank you, Jesus.
In Jesus' name,

Amen

Healthy Lifestyle Tip – Visualize your success! See your right-sized body now. Look to the future.

KNOW YOUR NUMBERS!

Day 18

Mark 5:28
For she said, If I may touch but his clothes, I shall be whole.

While we are in the battle of our lives to eat healthily, we must know our numbers. Joshua knew how many people he was going to fight against. Jesus knew he had to feed 5000 men, plus women and children. He also knew he was only working with five loaves of bread and two fish.

The lady with the issue of blood knew she had her condition for 12 years (Luke 8:43-48). Then there was the crippled man who knew he was at the pool of Bethesda for 38 years waiting to get in to be healed (John 5:1-17).

What are the numbers and readings of your BMI, A1C, cholesterol, blood pressure, and sugar glucose? Although the number on the scale does not define who we are, do you know how much you weigh? Be informed. Speak to your doctor, get a blood test, and get an understanding of the health of your body. Knowing your numbers can save your life. When we know our exact numbers, we can change our eating habits to lower them. How much progress have we made in the last 10, 30, 60, or 90 days? Record your weight loss as you follow a plan to win with food.

The woman with the issue of blood for 12 years was tired of feeling sick. She pushed her way through the crowd and touched the hem of Jesus' garment because she knew Jesus could heal her. She was sick and tired of being sick! The man sat at the pool for 38 years and told Jesus he wanted to be healed. Are we tired of the excess weight on our bodies? Do we want less of us on our bodies? Let's make the change! Push! Let's get it done!

Remember, the number on the scale does not define us. Many of us do not know or want to know how much we weigh. Get an accurate measurement of your weight by measuring yourself. By implementing a nutritious diet and regular exercise, it is possible to reduce that number.

Jesus healed people with many ailments and diseases. Is a healing touch needed today? Obesity, diabetes, and high blood pressure are diseases that are often related to weight. Losing weight often helps with the eradication of these diseases. Ask your doctor for a clear understanding of your health. Believe and put your faith into action and subscribe to a healthy weight loss plan, which might heal and make us well.

Dear Lord Jesus,

Touch me, Lord Jesus, with your healing hands! Give me the mind, Lord, to change my unhealthy eating choices and habits. Please heal my diseases. Please touch me, Lord.
In Jesus' name, Amen

Healthy Lifestyle Tip: Keep a food diary or journal of your health and weight loss numbers, daily food plans, comments, and thoughts.

WHAT IS YOUR NAME?

Day 19

II Corinthians 5:21
For he hath made him to be sin for us, who knew no sin; that we might
be made the righteousness of God in him.

Names such as "Fatty," "Porky the Pig," "Fatzilla," "Thunder thighs," "Ducky Butt," "Tub of Lard," "Fatso," and "Porky" are just a few insulting and hurtful names people have used to mock and belittle those who are obese and overweight. Believe it or not, some of us call these names to ourselves. God does not call His children these or anyone other demeaning names. The above names are not on our birth certificates. If any of those names or a similar one is your nickname, refuse to answer or respond to such names.

What does God call you? God calls us His children, joint heirs with Christ (Romans 8:17), his sons and daughters (2 Corinthians 6:18), and the righteousness of God (2 *Corinthians* 5:21). Do any of these names sound demeaning? Of course not. I am the righteousness of God, not a fatty! Yes, I have excess weight on my body, but I do not have to call myself a name. Be kind to yourself.

People may say whatever they want or think, you do not have to listen or accept what has been said. What we say to ourselves is what matters. Speak life! Do not engage in name-calling to oneself. Say your birth name. Those other names do not define who you are. We are children of the most-high God. I am the righteousness of God. Walk as you know it. Eat like you know it. Live as you believe it. Amen and amen. Go with God!

Dear Heavenly Father,

I am the righteousness of God. You call me a friend. I am in the beloved. Names that do not edify me shall not come from my lips. Let not the demeaning names that others have for me define who I am. You said I am the righteousness of God. You said that I am your son or daughter. Please help me remember what you call me and walk in it.
In Jesus' name,

Amen

Healthy Lifestyle Tip – Try an unfamiliar fruit. i.e., dragon fruit, papaya, Buddha's hand, lychee, pomelo, or gooseberries.

LIFT UP YOUR HANDS
Day 20

Lamentations 3:41
Let us lift up our heart with our hands unto God in the heavens.

Our hands can do many things. We can lift them to the Lord in praise, bring them together to pray in humble submission, and clap while rejoicing in song. We also use our hands to choose our foods, cook, plate our foods, and place food into our mouths. Also, many of us need to lift our hands to the Lord in surrendering our food issues and other things that weigh us down emotionally (our problems), physically (excess weight), and mentally (our negative thoughts). Unfortunately, our hands help us overeat, binge eat, stuff our mouths, and uncontrollably feed our faces. It's not worth the weight. Lord, help us!

Jesus used His hands to give sight to the blind, heal the sick, throw the moneychangers out of the synagogue, perform miracles, and make items as a carpenter. He used his hands for good. Let's respect and do good for our bodies when we use our hands to feed ourselves.

Our hands are an extension of our bodies, and they operate based on what we tell them to do. Like Jesus, let us use our hands to do good. Feed the poor, serve in ministry, and worship, for example. Let's also lift our hands in surrender to the Lord for those things we need to give to Him. Surrender our emotional eating to Him. Many of us need the Lord's help in this area when we are stressed, facing conflict, nervous, depressed, tired, or anxious.

Lift our hands in prayer as we seek His face in all things. Lift those hands in worship in our quiet time with Him and/or in the worship service, if this is your practice. Lift your hands. Surrender your food plan, your helplessness, and your cravings to the Lord.

Lift up your hands to the Lord!

Dear Lord,

I praise you today because of who you are. There is none like you. I lift my hands in submission, surrender, and offer my praise in all things. As I eat with my hands, let my hands choose those foods that will do my body good and not harm. "So, I will bless you as long as I live, in your name I will lift my hands" (Psalm 63:4 ESV).
In Jesus' name,

Amen

Healthy Lifestyle Tip – Try a new, easy recipe that aligns with your healthy lifestyle and food plan.

SALT THE EARTH
Day 21

Matthew 5:13
Ye are the salt of the earth: but if the salt have lost his savour,
wherewith shall it be salted? it is thenceforth good for nothing, but to
be cast out, and to be trodden under foot of men.

Who remembers the scientific name and molecular formula for salt? If you said sodium chloride or NaCl, you are correct. Salt has many purposes, one of which is to add flavor. Cooks often salt their dishes to bring out the flavor. Salt changes the taste of food. Most foods lack salt and need just a pinch or more to make them better. Be mindful of the amount of salt placed in and on top of your foods, and note the salt content inside packaged foods. Read the food labels for salt content.

Salt holds water in our bodies. We do not need additional weight. Release the water! Limit salt. Cinnamon, cumin, basil, rosemary, paprika, and fresh garlic are wonderful spices and herbs to flavor food. Citrus fruits are a great flavor enhancer too. Lemons are a personal favorite.

The Bible says we are the salt of the earth. Do our Christian walk and spoken words bring salt to the earth? Are we living holy and acceptable lives unto the Lord? As Christians, the Lord commands us in Matthew 5 to salt the earth. Our goal as Christians is to be the salt of the earth and let our words and lives bring glory to God.

Do our words and thoughts about healthy eating encourage us on this healthy eating journey? Watch the words that we say to ourselves. Let's flavor the earth with our kind words and live lives that reflect Christ and His message. Generously salt the earth, not your food.

Dear Lord,

To salt the earth is my desire, Lord. I ask for strength, power, and the willingness to do just that. Please help me be mindful of the salt I place in my foods and the heavy-laden salt-packaged foods I purchase. Hear my prayer, O Lord. In Jesus' name,

Amen

Healthy Lifestyle Tip – Be mindful of the daily intake of salt. Read the food labels for the salt content in foods and packaged foods. Salt retains water in the body. Consider a salt substitute or herbs. (Consult your doctor.)

CAST YOUR CARES

Day 22

I Peter 5:7 (ESV)
Casting all your anxieties on him, because he cares for you.

Are you loaded down with the heavy burdens of being overweight? Are life's troubles getting you down and making you sad? The Bible has the solution for each one of us. It's not a pill, mantra, exercise, or regimen. The Bible simply tells us to cast all our cares on Him. This may seem too easy, but it is difficult for some of us to lay down our burdens at the feet of Jesus. The burden of weight is physical, and we carry it around every minute. The burden of weight can be mental as well. We have tried every diet out there and still no success. Now, we are on another weight loss journey, and this time, we will get it right.

Give your cares to the Lord. (Psalm 55:22) Submit to the Lord and He will help us. He is concerned about everything that goes on in our lives, even weight loss. Lean on the everlasting arms of Jesus. He will carry us through.

Never forget to take your burdens to the Lord and leave them at His feet. What burdens and problems are you holding onto today? Weight is only one of many problems. Release them. In Matthew 11:30, the Lord said, *For my yoke is easy and my burden is light.* Give those burdens to the Lord. Now! Do not wait. Who wants to carry a heavy load? We are already carrying the weight of fat. Why are we carrying a load of burdens, too? If someone else wants to carry it, here it is. Jesus explicitly said to give Him our burdens, and in our case, that means excess weight. Praise the Lord. Lift and unload the burdens and excess weight. Lay them at the feet of Jesus.

Dear Lord,

I humbly lift my voice to you today. I know am supposed to cast all of my cares on you, but sometimes I forget to do so. Because of my circumstances, I sometimes forget to lay my burdens down at your feet. I know you can handle each of my circumstances and situations. I lay my burdens at your feet. They're yours, Lord. Thank you.
In the precious name of Jesus,

Amen

Healthy Lifestyle Tip – Cook and eat at home! Limit restaurant eating. Cooking at home allows the knowledge of what ingredients are in the food and control of food portions.

A TRANSFORMATION
Day 23

Romans 12:2
And be not conformed to this world: but be ye transformed by the
renewing of your mind, that ye may prove what is that good, and
acceptable, and perfect, will of God.

Transformation! Think of the many people in the Bible whose lives have been transformed because they had an encounter with Jesus. Paul, Rahab, the woman with the issue of blood, and Zacchaeus are a few of these people. Nicodemus asked Jesus how he could be reborn. He wanted a changed life, but he did not know how.

Fast forward to the 21st century. Name people you know who have had a transformed life because they met Jesus. Put my name on the list. Thanks be to God for His transforming power.

How many before and after pictures have you seen of people who have lost weight? Some magazines begin each new year with these before and after pictures. Some of us use the new year to change our lives with a healthy lifestyle. What an inspiration and encouragement these pictures bring! Do we want a set of these pictures in our photo album depicting our new bodies?

In today's scripture, Paul discusses the importance of transforming our minds and not conforming to the ways of the world. Let us apply this transformational mindset to our bodies as well, making small changes to our eating habits. These incremental changes will eventually culminate in significant improvements to our overall health. Take the initiative to make a positive change today.

Visualize yourself in a right-sized body, feeling and looking good. Witness your high blood pressure readings gradually returning to normal, experience less pressure on your knee joints, and the shedding of excess weight! Can you imagine confidently fastening the airplane seat belt without needing a seatbelt extender? Absolutely! Picture the potential of your doctor reducing or eliminating your medications. Barring other problems, this achievement is possible through embracing positive changes. The transformation of your body is attainable, and though it may take time, the weight is steadily departing from your body.

Jesus can help us. It involves our thinking about food and how perceive ourselves. By asking for God's help, believing in His power, receiving His grace, and letting Him transform us, we can change.

Dear Lord,
I humbly come before you, asking for help as I transform my body inside and out. I plan to stick to a new lifestyle change. Please renew my mind. Thank you, Lord.
In Jesus' name,
Amen.

Healthy Lifestyle Tip – Post before, present, and future pictures of yourself, depicting your starting point, current progress, and future self. Use an old photo or draw a picture of your future self for motivation.

ONE DAY AT A TIME

Day 24

Matthew 6:34 (NIV)
Therefore do not worry about tomorrow, for tomorrow will worry about itself. Each day has enough trouble of its own.

The Bible says we are not to worry about tomorrow. Worry, stress, and anxiety are all related. Stress also hampers weight loss. Let it go. Stress steals our joy and so much more. Why take on tomorrow's problems? There are so many problems today. Give your problems and cares to Jesus.

For most of those on a weight loss journey, the journey will not be a one-month journey. For some, the journey may be as long as a year or more. No matter the timeframe, take each day as it comes. Do not worry about next week, next month, or next year. Do not worry about the next weigh-in. For those who weigh in once a month, a month of worry about the next weigh-in is a lot of worrying. Be present and take care of today! Eat right for today; focus on one day at a time and one meal at a time.

Stress hinders weight loss. Worrying and being stressed can even add weight to your body. Be calm. Do the work. Stressed? Pray and ask God for direction and then leave the situation in His hands. Walk the stress off. Are you worrying about something? Talk to God if you lack wisdom. If you lack wisdom about your weight loss journey, seek guidance from a professional, doctor, nutritionist, mentor, or food coach for help. After eating the wrong portion size of protein, it's done! The food is inside your body. Be mindful of the next meal. Move on.

To achieve success in managing our meals and weight, it is crucial to plan our daily meals the night before or on the morning of the day. Use a meal planning app, paper notebook or journal, calendar, or kitchen whiteboard to plan meals. Personally, I find it convenient to use the Note section on my smartphone to organize and write my meals, allowing me to review past menus for inspiration. Whether you prefer planning for the entire week or focusing on daily meal plans, consistency is key. Just as excess weight accumulated gradually, shedding it requires patience and a steady approach. Slow and steady progress leads to lasting results. Take it one day at a time.

Dear Lord,

I take each day and meal one step at a time. While keeping the finish line in sight, I rely on your daily guidance. I pray that each meal nourishes and keeps me until the next one.
In Jesus' name,
Amen

Healthy Lifestyle Tip – Do not stress over having to lose _____ pounds. Focus on one day at a time and one pound at a time. Choose small goals with obtainable benchmarks.

WEARY?

Day 25

II Thessalonians 3:13
But ye, brethren, be not weary in well doing.

A re you weary and tired of eating clean and you want to eat a specific indulgent food item like _____? (Name your guilty pleasure.) Some diets may permit cheat days or occasional indulgences to satisfy cravings. Moderation is key. If your weight loss plan accommodates it, enjoying a "cheat" meal can provide a sense of upliftment. After all, nobody wants to experience weariness on this journey.

Weariness will sometimes break down our discipline. Do not give up. Don't stop. Ask God for additional strength and take away the weariness. Can you see any benefits of losing weight and the new healthy weight loss plan? Focus on those things. Yes, we want what we want when we want it. Self-gratification got us into the trouble we are in now. Let's not regress. Do not get weary while doing good. Press on. Keep going. If you cheat with one meal, it will not kill you.

However, if you cannot get back on track with the next meal, I suggest you leave those cravings and cheat days alone.

Restrictive food plans often bring about weariness. The healthy eating journey can bring about weariness, especially when others are eating the foods that you want and enjoy. Eat those foods that will keep you on the journey. Make sure your food plan has a variety of food items with colorful options. For example, a white fish with cauliflower and white asparagus may taste great, but may not be appealing to the eye.

Ask the Savior to help you overcome weariness. Old eating habits got us into trouble, but staying the course will bring rewards. There is help for your weary soul. Remember why we are on the journey. My friends, *"Be not weary in well doing."* Your body will reap the benefits. Stay the course.

Dear Lord,

Sometimes I'm weary and tired of sticking to the plan. I know what is right for my body. This food plan and my simple changes to my eating have helped me. Please remind me of this. If I need to change my food plan, please give knowledge and understanding to my coach and/or my mentor.
In Jesus' name,

Amen

Healthy Lifestyle Tip – Drink green tea, and not with refined sugar.

THE LUST OF THE EYE

Day 26

I John 2:16
For all that is in the world, the lust of the flesh, and the lust of the eyes,
and the pride of life, is not of the Father, but is of the world.

Each day, we make decisions about what we eat. What influences those choices? Having a food plan for the day helps with this, but when you see beautiful, plated, appealing foods on a television commercial, cooking show, billboard, at a restaurant, on family members' plates, or even at the supermarket, many of us want to eat them. I do! Do we want them because we see them? We eat with our eyes. Chefs make food look appealing to eat on the plate and the aroma of the food piques our sense of smell. Food stylists prepare and style food to be appealing. Food packaging is to encourage the consumer to purchase the product.

Choices! We have to eat, and food is not bad, but how the food is prepared and the quantity of it is often the problem. Ask yourself these questions. Will this food help me reach my goals? Is this food on my food plan today? Are the butter, whole milk, sugar, salt, and/or all-purpose flour content in the food item good for me? While certain food choices may be acceptable to others, they may not always be suitable for you. Exercise caution when selecting your meal. Today, we are discussing food choices, but be mindful of desires and temptations in all areas of life. Covetousness, greed, jealousy, unlawful sex, and gluttony are just examples that warrant careful consideration.

The fruit that Eve saw in the garden was pleasing to the eye. That was not a sin. The fruit was pleasing to the eye because God made the fruit and created the beautiful Garden of Eden, which included the Tree of Knowledge of Good and Evil. However, Eve wanted something that God told her she could not have, which was anything from the Tree of Knowledge of Good and Evil. She wanted and ate the forbidden fruit, and gave some to Adam. A sinful act occurred, and they paid dearly for going against God's Word. We are still paying for the consequences of that sin today. Be mindful of the lust of the eye.

Dear God,

You are my help and strength. Walk with me as I yield not to the lust of the eye. Please give me the mind and strength not to deviate from my food plan. I draw from your strength today.
In Jesus' name,
Amen

Healthy Lifestyle Tip – Form a habit of sitting down at the table while eating. Elevate the presentation of your meal using lovely plates, placemats, and bowls.

FOLLOW THE PLAN

Day 27

Proverbs 16:3 (NIV)
Commit to the LORD whatever you do, and he will establish your
plans.

A weight loss regimen is a set of rules about food and exercise that some people follow in order to stay healthy. [1] For weight loss and for a healthy lifestyle of living, a daily regimen is very necessary. Some regimens are strict and others are of a more relaxed nature. Some regimens have many rules and others a few, but there is a plan to live by. Planning is key, but one must know the written plan, understand it and then follow it. For example, daily follow the Keto diet plan and walk for 30 minutes every morning at 6:30 AM five days a week. There are many diets and exercise regimens, but choose one that meets your lifestyle and needs. Can you follow the plan and is it sustainable?

Is there a plan for spiritual growth and personal time with The Lord? Consistently spending time with God in prayer and Bible

54

study keeps our hearts in tune with Him. Plan your time with God. Will this happen in the morning before the start of the day or at the conclusion of the day? Maybe after the children go to school or during their nap time. Choose a time that works for your lifestyle. Not choosing a time to spend with God allows other things to take precedence, and time with God doesn't happen. Read His Word, pray, and listen.

Have a regimen of diet and exercise, but do not forget about personal time with the Lord. So where does our personal time with the Lord fit into the schedule and when and where is the exercise plan being carried out? Is there a written plan for weight loss? Know the plan and execute it! Benefits from a spiritual regimen, exercise, and diet equal growing with Jesus and weight loss.

Dear Lord,

So glad I make time to spend with you each day. In your presence is the fullness of joy. I love our time together. Please give me the mind to want to stick to my weight loss plan and exercise regimen and turn my health around. Help me glorify you in my body and healthy eating habits.
In Jesus' name,

Amen

Healthy Lifestyle Tip – Stick to an exercise and healthy eating routine. Be consistent and show up for yourself!

THE FUTURE ME
Day 28

Proverbs 29:18
Where there is no vision, the people perish: but he that keepeth the law,
happy is he.

P icture yourself in the future. Can you imagine the physical transformation that your body will undergo if you maintain a commitment to healthy eating? Older pictures can serve as reminders of our previous selves when we carried less weight on our bodies. Let's be honest here. We are not referring to pictures from an excessively distant time in our youth, but rather images from before the weight accumulated or from earlier years when successful weight loss was achieved.

Yes, I can! This excess weight is leaving me. I can do all things with Christ. The vision of myself in my right-sized body will happen soon. The Bible says in I Thessalonians 5:24, *Faithful is he that calleth you, who also will do it.* He has called you to be faithful. Let us do our best. God has been faithful to us in every way. Be faithful to your weight loss journey. Show up. Do the work, but it is difficult, you may say. Yes, it is!

Make sure your weight loss plan includes foods you love and enjoy. Many years ago, in the 1970s, eating liver was mandatory once a week on the Weight Watchers diet program. Then and now, liver is not on my favorite food list, and I have not eaten liver ever since. Eat foods you enjoy. While fried chicken may not be suitable for a meal plan five times a week, using an Air Fryer can make it a viable option. God wants us to be wise with our food choices and portion size. We need a vision, as emphasized in today's scripture reference. See the vision of yourself. Keep up the work because the transformation of your body is on its way. Remember, your body is slowly changing every day as you put in the effort. Eat healthily!

Dear Lord,

You are faithful and dependable. I will stand on your Word. Thanks for your faithfulness to me. Faithfully, I will try to show up every day to follow my weight loss plan and good eating habits. I see the vision of myself without the excess weight. Help me do this to your glory and not for my vain glory.
In Jesus' name,

Amen

Healthy Lifestyle Tip – Stress can hinder weight loss. Let it go! Eliminate stress from your life.

FUEL FOR THE BODY

Day 29

II Samuel 17:29 (ESV)
Honey and curds and sheep and cheese from the herd, for David and
the people with him to eat, for they said, "The people are hungry and
weary and thirsty in the wilderness.

We have to eat, right? Yes! Food is fuel and nourishment for the body. So, enjoy your food and eat, but not at any cost. The problem is what and when we eat, and how much of it. Our scripture today lists the meal of David and the people with him. They ate honey, butter, sheep, and cheese. Why? They were hungry, weary, and thirsty while traveling in the wilderness. So, they ate! God created our bodies to need nourishment each day. When we add too much nourishment (calories), our bodies store the extra calories that are not burned and turn them into fat. Lord, why is this so? I perceive the Lord's voice, emphasizing the significance of upholding boundaries and balance in my approach to food.

If honey, cheese, and butter are not on your food plan, as in our scripture verse today, there are hundreds of other foods. There are vegan options and substitutions. Do the research.

As we fuel our bodies, remember, we must also feast on the Word of God. Reading God's Word spiritually feeds us daily. We never can get too much of the Word of God. Every day, we need to feast on God's Word and pray. Be fat on the Word. Fill up on God's Word. Eat food to fuel and give energy to the body and partake of God's Word for the soul. Yes, Lord!

Dear Lord,

Nourishing my soul and body is my goal. I will feast unlimitedly on your Word and eat only the daily food requirements for my physical body. Thank you for the food that I purchase, cook, and eat. Also, thanks for the healthy takeout too.
In Jesus' name,

Amen

Healthy Lifestyle Tip – Speak affirmations.

"I am on my way to my right-sized body."

"I can do this weight loss journey. God is helping me."

"I know the past is the past, and I will move forward with healthy eating."

DON'T GET WEARY!

Day 30

Galatians 6:9 (NIV)
Let us not become weary in doing good, for at the proper time we will
reap a harvest if we do not give up.

While our scripture reference may not directly relate to weight loss, there may be moments when we grow weary of eating nutritious foods and exercising. Raise your hand if get you tired of eating the right foods, which are good for our bodies. Our bodies appreciate the great choices we make, and we will witness and experience positive results as long as we stay on the path to healthy living. Don't get weary! Keep going. Your efforts will pay off.

Our bodies will reap what we put into them. Green vegetables, fruits, and wise portions aid us in weight loss. It's also important not to overlook fiber-rich vegetables and fruits. Seven to nine hours of sleep aids in weight loss. The hydration that occurs with 6-8 eight-ounce cups of water will reap enormous health benefits. Our bodies want what was just mentioned.

We reap what we sow into ourselves. Jesus may not have been talking about our healthy lifestyle, but the principle is the same. We reap what we sow. Do you want a healthy body and not be at risk for certain diseases?

Feeling weary of maintaining a healthy diet? Reflect on what carrying excess weight on your body feels like. As the author of this devotional, I can testify that having shed 80 pounds, I experience a remarkable sense of lightness. My steps are lighter, going up the stairs is much easier, and I can play tennis in my 60s for long periods. Despite the temptation to indulge in those 900 calories of guilty pleasure, I know what living as I do feels like 24 hours a day. It's not worth the weight. Hallelujah, amen, and amen once again.

Dear Jesus,

My journey to healthy eating is my desire. I hope to respect my temple and feed it those foods that will do my body good. You are my help.
In Jesus' name,

Amen

Healthy Lifestyle Tip – Pray first and ask God for strength to stick with your healthy lifestyle change. Share your feelings of weariness. God will deliver your weariness. Later, call a friend, weight loss coach, or mentor for encouragement and support.

PRAYER and FASTING

Day 31

Mark 9:29
And he said unto them, This kind can come forth by nothing, but by
prayer and fasting.

To break strongholds, seek direction from the Lord. Seek discernment, gain victory, and get closer to God, and to do that, fasting can help. Some things only come forth by prayer and fasting. At designated times, give up the food and take up prayer. When we fast, we are giving up food, to varying degrees, for a time in order to focus on prayer and being alone with God.

Fasting can be for any period of time—one meal, two meals together (breakfast and lunch), one day, or even longer. The time period is up to you as you listen to God. But, however long you decide to fast, this type of spiritual fasting needs to be planned and not announced to others, because fasting is also between you and God.

Have you ever considered fasting to gain spiritual renewal or direction from the Lord? For some of you, fasting may be difficult, but prayer and fasting will take the focus off of food and place it where it belongs—onto God.

Were you aware that Daniel practiced fasting while only eating fruits and vegetables (Daniel 10:3)? We know this fasting method as the Daniel Fast. Daniel abstained from eating any animal products. While the primary purpose of the Daniel Fast is spiritual, it may lead to weight loss. Some individuals choose to adopt a similar diet daily.

Jesus (Matthew 4:2), Moses (Exodus 34:38) Elijah (I Kings 19), and Paul (II Corinthians 11:27) all fasted. Esther, her attendants, and the Jews in Susa fasted for three days and three nights before she approached the King (Esther 4:16). Esther needed direction from God. There are many types of spiritual fasts. Research spiritual fasts and the benefits of spiritual renewal.

Barnabas, Nehemiah, Ezra, Jonah, and Prophetess Anna are a few more people in the Bible that also fasted. Each one fasted for different reasons, and God met them in their fasts. Consider fasting one meal a week. This is not an occasion to eat more later. We give up our food for the length of the fast. Pray during the time of fasting and seek God's face. Spiritual fasting is unnecessary for weight loss, but it can be an integral part of our spiritual walk.

Dear Lord,

Blessed to be on this weight loss journey of eating healthy and adopting good eating habits. Although I may struggle on this journey, at some point, I will fast from a meal or meals to get closer to you, seek direction, and spend time more time with you.
In Jesus' name,
Amen

Healthy Lifestyle Tip – Try the Daniel Fast for spiritual renewal.

CONSISTENCY IS KEY

Day 32

I Corinthians 15:58 (NIV)
Therefore, my dear brothers and sisters, stand firm. Let nothing move
you. Always give yourselves fully to the work of the Lord, because you
know that your labor in the Lord is not in vain.

Jesus' message and His life were always consistent. Hebrews
13:8 emphasizes that Jesus remains the same yesterday, today,
and forever - a steadfast beacon of hope and guidance. While
it is true that Jesus is divine, we are called to follow His
example. Follow His footsteps.

Consistency is the key to success in your weight loss journey. It
requires showing up every day and sticking to your plan. Avoid the
trap of one day on and one day off or taking the weekends off. Just as
in our prayer life and personal devotions, being consistent every day
yields significant growth.

Many seen and unseen challenges may come while on this
weight loss journey. Be ready for them. What is the plan if those

challenges show up? For example, getting caught outside of the house during your mealtime without your planned food. How will you handle this challenge? Will I forget my weight loss plan for today and start over tomorrow? I think not. Plan how you will handle this before it happens.

Do not give up on your goal of losing the excess weight on your body. With all the excuses, challenges, pitfalls, naysayers, food pushers, cravings, scale disappointments, sadness, bumps in the road, difficulties, triumphs, victories, and great eating habits that may come, at all costs, try to stay consistent. Stay focused on the journey. Consistency is one key to weight loss success. Prioritize and support yourself on this healthy journey. Invest in you with consistency! Your health matters.

Dear Lord,

My prayer today is that I remain consistent in all that I do. I choose to be consistent in my prayer and devotional life, weight loss journey, exercising 5-6 times a week, ministry obligations, and anything else on my agenda. Faithful to the tasks, goals, and obligations is my desire.
Lead me and guide me, dear Lord, I pray.
In Jesus' name,

Amen

Healthy Lifestyle Tip – Refrain from eating between meals except for planned snacks.

EAT THE FRUIT

Day 33

Haggai 2:19
Is the seed yet in the barn? yea, as yet the vine, and the fig tree, and the
pomegranate, and the olive tree, hath not brought forth: from this day
will I bless you.

In Genesis 2, God told Adam and Eve that they could eat anything in the Garden of Eden except fruit from the Tree of Knowledge of Good and Evil. Since God created many fruits, God wanted Adam and Eve to eat fruit, just not from the forbidden tree. Fruit is not bad for us; fruit holds many health benefits for us. As stated in an earlier devotional, Adam and Eve went against God's plan for them. God has blessed us with many species of fruit to eat.

According to The Centers for Disease Control and Prevention, we should eat 1.5 to 2 cups of fruit daily.[1] Fresh fruit is key, but flash-frozen fruit in the freezer section of your supermarket embodies significant benefits too. Eat from over 2000 species of fruit. All fruits are edible, except give or take 80 of them. Therefore, we have so many options for fruit consumption. Fruits have such great nutritious value and offer color to our plates. Fruit provides vitamins, fiber, and minerals. Although fruit contains natural sugar, most fruit is low in fat and calories. For example, apples have potassium, vitamin C, and fiber. Pomegranates have nutritional value, including potassium, vitamin C, zinc, and magnesium.

Today's scripture mentions pomegranates, olives, and figs. Every morning for breakfast, I eat pomegranate seeds with other colorful fruit for my health and enjoyment. My 6 oz morning bowl of fruit is colorful, healthy, tasty, and beautiful. Partake of the health benefits that fruit gives the human body. Eat what God has provided for your enjoyment, the health of your body, and fuel.

Dear Lord,

Thank you, Jesus, for the availability of fresh fruit accessible to some of us. Thanks for the different seasons that produce various fruits. I appreciate the vibrant colors, delightful aromas, distinct flavors, and the assortment of different sizes and shapes that fruit embodies. Thank you for these wonderful gifts.
In Jesus' name,

Amen

Healthy Lifestyle Tip – Eat at least two servings a day of fruit. Some weight loss plans allow for more. When you achieve your weight loss goal, it is possible to add additional servings of fruit.

FREEDOM IN CHRIST
Day 34

Galatians 5:1
Stand fast therefore in the liberty wherewith Christ hath made us free,
and be not entangled again with the yoke of bondage.

Food is a staple of life. There is nothing wrong with food. It's how we view, eat, cook our food, and handle our portions that can be the problem. Jesus talked about food and even cooked fish on top of coals at the Sea of Galilee for the disciples. God placed many trees in the Garden of Eden. Neutrality around food will aid in weight loss. Do not be a slave to food. Be liberated from the traps of certain foods that put excess weight on our bodies. The mention of a juicy steak can trigger some people into a tailspin. There is nothing wrong with a juicy ribeye steak, but a one-pound steak at dinner might be an excessive protein portion.

Have you called on Jesus when in trouble, and He came to your aid? Oh, the name of Jesus. There is no other name above His. Call on Him; He is present even for the emergency food situations that occur in our life.

Be free. Drop the chains of bondage to food. Who can release us? Who can break these chains? Ask the Savior for help. Add professional therapy for additional help with food issues. If a food coach, mentor, or nutritionist can assist you on your journey, acquire one. Some are free and others charge a fee. One day soon, we shall declare with joy, "I am free! I have cultivated a wonderful relationship with food. Excess weight and food no longer hold me in bondage."

Dear Lord,

Free me from the grip of food's stronghold. Let me not be a slave to unhealthy food choices. If I consume them, grant me moderation and the occasional indulgence. Help me break free from food bondage and regain control.
In the precious name of Jesus,

Amen

Healthy Lifestyle Tip – Be the queen, king, ruler, or manager of your temple. Make the right food choices.

MY HELP!

Day 35

Psalm 121:1-2
I will lift up mine eyes unto the hills, from whence cometh my help.
²My help cometh from the LORD, which made heaven and earth.

We need strength for today and every day. While on a weight loss journey and/or on a food plan, where does my help come from? Our help comes from the Lord who made heaven and earth. He is our helper!

For some, staying on a weight loss plan is easy. For others, staying on a plan is challenging. There is supernatural help available for choosing our food, cooking it, and eating it. God will lead us to resources to aid us. Every praise belongs to God and God alone.

Is help needed with our food issues, staying on the plan, and taking good care of our temple? Yes, there is hope and help for each of us. Is there anything too hard for God? (Jeremiah 32:27) No! Trust God; our help comes from the Lord. He knows all about our struggles and petitions.

70

I'll never forget asking a prayer warrior at a prayer service to pray for my bad eating habits. The unusual prayer request flabbergasted him, but he said nothing about it and prayed, anyway. God is concerned about any issue that concerns each of us. He hears our prayers and those that intercede for us in prayer. I began new eating habits to lose the excess weight, and the weight dropped.

Although we want to get to the end of the weight loss journey with our right-sized body right now, take this journey one meal at a time. Focus on today and its meals and exercise regime. Then tomorrow, take care of that day.

Ask for help from your heavenly Father and go to your doctor or nutritionist for earthly help. Heads up! God is our helper. Draw from the wisdom and strength that our heavenly Father provides. Your help comes from the Lord who made heaven and earth. Praise the Lord.

Dear Lord,

I lift my head with my eyes on you. My help and strength come from you. I rely on you. Your Word says to ask anything in your name. Lord, I need your help with managing my food and eating plan. Empower me today! I pray to live holy and walk healthier in your way! I take comfort in your help. Thank you, Lord.
In Jesus' name,

Amen

Healthy Lifestyle Tip – Eliminate refined sugar from your diet. Replace refined sugar with honey, agave, fruit purees, or maple sugar.

THE JOY THIEF
Day 36

John 10:10 ESV

The thief comes only to steal and kill and destroy. I came that they may have life and have it abundantly.

The thief comes to steal. Steal what? He comes to steal our health, joy, money, family, and life. We do not have to let him have any of it. We can change some of our health problems and issues through our diet, exercise, and lifestyle. There are so many diseases that are weight related. Since no one is shoving food into our mouths, let's be mindful of what and how much we eat.

Healthy eating can change our bodies today. We can improve our quality of life with the shedding of excess weight. Remember, food portion matters.

Losing weight will not fix all the problems in one's life, but it can give a better quality of life. Who wants to be winded every time you walk up a flight of stairs or have sleep apnea because of obesity?

Losing weight will not bring joy if there are other problems in one's life that need to be fixed. However, seeing and feeling lighter when the loss of weight leaves will put a smile on your face. Pray and ask God for His daily help on this weight loss journey and/or help with living a healthier lifestyle.

Since today's scripture states, *The thief comes only to steal and kill and destroy,* be on alert. Do not let the devil steal your joy. Jesus is speaking the words in today's verse: "I come that they may have life and more abundantly." Trust Jesus with your life, heart, food plan, and life eternal. Everyone must ask Jesus Christ into their hearts for life eternal.

Dear Lord,

Thank you Jesus for your Word today. That old devil wants to steal my joy, health, money, and life. I am on alert about his cunning ways. Lord, I give you my life, health, money, and joy. I want that abundant life that only you give. Thanks for dying on the cross and rising from the grave to give me that abundant life.
In the precious name of Jesus,

Amen

Healthy Lifestyle Tip – Stay hydrated. Drink water. Infuse your water with cucumbers, lemons, or limes.

THE FLESH SPEAKS

Day 37

Matthew 26:41 (NIV)
Watch and pray so that you will not fall into temptation. The spirit is
willing, but the flesh is weak.

Self-control, discipline, willpower, consistency, perseverance, and stick-to-itiveness are needed during a weight loss journey because the flesh is weak! The flesh wants what it wants and when it wants. Is this an excuse to feed our flesh what it wants? I think not.

We control what goes into our mouths. No one else decides and places food into our mouths but us. Sometimes there are family or friends who are food pushers, but no one can literally put the food in our mouth.

If choosing the wrong foods is a problem, talk to the Lord and a nutritionist about it! Encourage yourself with scripture about eating healthy. There are over 90 verses in this devotional book to support and encourage a weight loss journey. Speak out loud about what healthy eating is. Eat right! Visualize your right-sized body. Do you see the picture? Inside of you is a healthier version. Be strong in God's strength.

If we are hungry, our guard may be down when making food choices. Plan all meals before the start of the day. Today's scripture says our spirit is willing, but the flesh is weak. We often lack the strength or willpower to make excellent decisions when hungry. We need God's strength, direction, and a food plan to help us.

The flesh is weak in other areas of our lives, too. The flesh wants to sin. Crucify the flesh. The flesh wants what is contrary to God's desires for us.

Galatians 5:16-17 speaks about walking in the Spirit so that we won't give into the flesh. Since we were born into sin, our sinful nature wants us to sin. The sin of gluttony is not the only sin. Other sins of the flesh include sexual immorality, idolatry, hatred, discord, jealousy, fits of rage, selfish ambition, envy; drunkenness, to name a few. Galatians 5:19-20 (NIV) says, "Do not feed the flesh with lustful desires. Walk in the spirit, watch, and pray."

My Gracious Lord and Father,

Sometimes I find my flesh in conflict with the Spirit. Help!
I do not want to give into my flesh. Please bring my flesh into
subjection. I want to eat right and not overfeed my flesh. I need thee,
oh I need thee.
In the precious name of Jesus,

Amen

Healthy Lifestyle Tip – Never shop at the supermarket when hungry.

THIS DAY

Day 38

Psalm 118:24
This is the day which the Lord hath made; we will rejoice and be glad
in it.

A year has 365 days (except for leap years). Without exception, the length of each day is 24 hours, beginning at 12:00 AM and ending at 11:59 PM. When the twenty-four hours are over, a new day begins. Who put this all into motion? Who created the night, which turns into the morning? Who put the sun in its place and the moon to shine at night? No worldwide governmental committee constructed our days. Our heavenly Father put this in motion when He created the earth and the day. Although we have organized time, God is timeless and transcends time.

How many of you have seen the movie *Groundhog Day?* In this movie, each new day started over, just as it did the day before, repeating the events of the previous day. Finally, one day, a brand-new day occurred with new events.

The blessing about a new day is that if we mess up on a particular day, a new day begins at midnight to try again. For various reasons, there will be days where we will not follow our diet, food plan, or our healthy lifestyle as planned. Praise God, we can start over at the very next meal or the next day. God grants us a new day each morning to get it right.

Do not wait for a new week, month, season, or year to start again. New mercies, a new day, and new beginnings are ours. We will bless the Lord every day. We will rejoice in the day. Yes, even if we are obese, overweight, or just need a few pounds to lose, The Bible says rejoice. We are on a journey to fix our bodies. There are no contingencies. Rejoice no matter what! Rejoice that we have the mind to change our ways and we are doing the work. Praise the Lord!

Dear Lord,

Give us this day our daily bread. Thanks for waking me up each morning and helping me through each day with my eating habits. When I lose my way by not eating those foods that will bless my body or overeat, please remind me that there is a next meal and a tomorrow to get it right. I rejoice in you!
In Jesus' name,

Amen

Healthy Lifestyle Tip – Start your day with breakfast. Break the overnight fast with breakfast.

CONFIDENCE IN HIM

Day 39

I John 5:14
And this is the confidence that we have in him, that, if we ask any thing according to his will, he heareth us:

The Lord hears the voice of his children calling out to Him. He hears us and listens to our petitions. Have you ever spoken to someone, and they didn't hear a word you said? Why? They may have been on their phone, on social media, asleep, or just preoccupied. This is not the case with our Lord and Savior. The Bible says that we are to know and have the confidence that He hears us, whatever we ask of him.

Take everything to the Lord in prayer. Go in confidence knowing He hears. Also, go in confidence that He will aid and help during your food struggles. Lean on Jesus when you struggle with eating right. You can ask or say anything to Him!

You could say:

"Lord, help me stay on course."

"Lord, please help me not to binge eat."

"When I get weary of this food struggle of eating healthily, help!"

"Lord, please help me enjoy the journey."

Jesus did not have a weight problem. But He is concerned about all that concerns us, large or small. Jesus wants us in a right-sized body. However, He will not love us any less if we are obese, overweight, or have extra pounds on our bodies. I Samuel 16:7 states, "But the Lord said to Samuel, 'Do not consider his appearance or his height, for I have rejected him. The Lord does not look at the things people look at. People look at the outward appearance, but the Lord looks at the heart.'"

Go in the confidence of the Lord. Be filled with the assurance of the Lord. We've got confidence!

Dear Lord,

I come to thee asking for help. No other help, I know. My prayer is that I stay steadfast on this weight loss journey. I want to honor you in my temple. I am confident that I can lose this excess weight, stay and live a healthy lifestyle. This is my prayer!
In Jesus' name,

Amen

Healthy Lifestyle Tip – Celebrate every win, big or small.

TEMPTATION 2.0
Day 40

Matthew 4:2-3 (ESV)
And after fasting forty days and forty nights, he was hungry. ³And the
tempter came and said to him, "If you are the Son of God, command
these stones to become loaves of bread."

Satan had a conversation with Jesus after His 40-day fast. Really Satan? Satan thought he could tempt Jesus? Sorry, Satan. You were mistaken. Satan steered Adam and Eve, others in the Bible, and many people of today in the wrong direction, but not the Lord Jesus Christ.

Verse 2 of Matthew 4 states that Jesus was hungry after fasting for forty days and forty nights. How many of us have difficulty fasting for one meal? Our hunger pains or lack of discipline often take over. Satan tempted the Lord by asking Him to use His power to turn stones into bread and conqueror His hunger. (Bread is the author's trigger food.)

Jesus possessed the divine power to reject Satan's request, as He is God. If Jesus yielded to Satan's request, our salvation would have lost all meaning. In Matthew 4:10; Jesus said, *Away from me, Satan. For it is written: Worship the Lord your God and serve him only.*

Many temptations do not originate from Satan; instead, they arise from our own cravings and desires. Whenever I step into specific supermarkets, I find myself surrounded by enticing food items that I love but are heavy-laden with high calories. I call on the name of Jesus and keep it moving. Isn't the produce section meant to be the first department as you enter the supermarket? If this is not a particular struggle for you, other temptations may confront you. Resist those foods you have not gained control over, whether by limiting your intake or avoiding them altogether, to prevent excess weight.

Jesus knows each of us by name and understands our struggles. Ask the Savior for help in conquering challenges. Just as Jesus resisted Satan and His own flesh, let's choose to stand against temptation and the cravings that assail us. To support us, remember to stay hydrated by drinking water, seek ways to manage stress, and avoid going to the supermarket on an empty stomach. With Jesus' strength and guidance, we can overcome our struggles and lead a more balanced and healthy life.

Dear Lord, my Savior, and King,

With your strength and guidance, I can overcome my struggles and temptations. I look to you.
In Jesus' name,
Amen

Healthy Lifestyle Tip – Name your trigger foods. Keep them out of sight, out of the house if possible, and out of your hands and mouth.

OUR REFUGE and STRENGTH

Day 41

Psalm 46:1
God is our refuge and strength, a very present help in trouble.

Not everyone is changing their lives to a healthier lifestyle or starting a weight loss journey because they want to look better in jeans or a bathing suit. Some people are in trouble! Medical trouble. Some have to lose weight for an upcoming surgery, others are pre-diabetic, others are an unhealthy weight that affects their daily living and heart health, and others have high cholesterol. These are only some reasons.

When the doctor states weight loss is necessary to avoid the use of insulin needles or the onset of disease, trouble is at hand and there is a significant health concern. When in trouble, where can you run to for help? We can run straight to Christ Jesus. Refuge for my soul! We can take refuge in the Lord because He promised never to leave or forsake us. God will never leave us alone. Then we must do the work of losing the weight. Isaiah 43:2 states, *When thou passest through the waters, I will be with thee; and through the rivers, they shall not overflow thee: when thou walkest through the fire, thou shalt not be burned; neither shall the flame kindle upon thee.* When we pass through dark times and deep waters, He promised to be right there for us. We can take refuge in our Savior. Why? If we go to friends, family, and strangers, they may fail us and not meet our expectations.

Since the Lord already told us to take refuge in Him, we can do this journey with Him. He has the ability, power, and wherewithal to keep us during our food struggles. He can keep us from falling, too (Jude 24). God is not only our refuge but our strength as well. We can do this. God has us. When we are weak, He is strong for us. He is always present. He's never a no-show. God is our refuge and strength. Tell the doctor, "I will lose weight by our next visit. I want to live! I will subscribe to a healthier lifestyle." Lean on Jesus. Our strength is in the Lord. Take refuge in Him.

Dear Lord,

So glad I can find refuge in you. Where can I flee? I run to you, O Lord. I can hide and be with you, my refuge and strength. Thanks be to God for this help!
In Jesus' name,

Amen

Healthy Lifestyle Tip – Do not let food pushers (family, friends, or unknown people) sway you to eat foods that are not on your plan or are not the right choice for you.

COVET NOT!
Day 42

Hebrews 13:5
Let your conversation be without covetousness; and be content with such things as ye have: for he hath said, I will never leave thee, nor forsake thee.

Covetousness! I want her body. My friend can eat whatever she wants, not gain weight, and still look good. Why do I have to work so hard to lose one pound? My friend, work with what you have. Yes, genetics, sleep patterns, metabolism, stress, lack of hydration, and foods chosen are just some components that impede the loss of weight. Be content.

It is not uncommon for some individuals to feel down or depressed when on a weight loss journey. It's disheartening to witness others enjoying their favorite foods, while you must be mindful of your choices. You can still eat foods you enjoy, but be mindful of portion sizes and choose healthier alternatives when possible.

You are not alone on this journey. Forty-five million people go on a diet every year.[1] Not all of them continue, but there is a remnant that stays on this journey. Find a friend who will walk with you on this journey.

Be glad you and the Lord are on the weight loss journey together. Whatever the situation, hear the voice of the Lord reminding you with His Word that He will never leave or forsake you.

Find contentment with your food plan, ensuring that you enjoy the meals it offers. While some foods may not be suitable for you at this time, remember that it doesn't mean they are off-limits forever. Keep your focus on your nourishing and satisfying plate of food and the steps you are making toward wellness.

Some of our friends and/or family members who started the weight loss journey with us may have abandoned the journey. Remember, Jesus is with us when we exercise, eat, sleep, during times of food temptation, and even when we get on the scale. We have a promise from God that He will never leave us. This is our promise, and God never breaks a promise. His promises are yes and Amen.

Dear Lord,

I hear your words spoken by the Apostle Paul: "I will never leave thee, nor forsake thee." I relish this promise. When I feel alone, I choose not to eat emotionally, and I hope to remember that your Word states I am not alone. You are with me, leading and guiding me. I am never alone.
In Jesus' name,

Amen

Healthy Lifestyle Tip – Instead of salt, flavor foods with fresh herbs, spices, and dried herbs.

LOVE, LOVE, L-O-V-E
Day 43

John 3:16
For God so loved the world, that he gave his only begotten Son, that whosoever believeth in him should not perish, but have everlasting life.

Love is a universal desire for most people. Many look for love in the wrong places and/or in the wrong things. Some people think because they are fat that there is so much to love, or they don't feel worthy of love. You are worthy of love. We can categorize love into three types: Eros, Philos (phileo), and Agape. Eros represents physical attraction or romantic love. Philos (phileo) signifies brotherly or friendly love. Agape embodies divine, godly love.

God loves us no matter what body shape, size, or weight. Others may not love us because of our size, but not God. Exhibit love for yourselves, despite the extra weight on our bodies. We are never to hate ourselves or our bodies, but continue to change our eating habits for the good of our temple. We must exhibit self-control in our eating.

No greater love existed than this. Jesus showed His love for us on the cross of Calvary. He shed His blood and life on Calvary to pay the price of sin and death on our behalf. There was no greater love than God sending his son to earth to be born a baby, and then become a man to die on the cross for our sins. There is no greater love! God loves us!

Do not forget to love yourself! Practice self-love. Love and take care of you! Change those things that you do not love about yourself. Avoid sabotaging your healthy lifestyle, diet plan, or food plan with bad thoughts about yourself and old, bad eating habits. God loved us so much that He sent His only son. He deems us worthy. Now let's take care of our bodies, souls, and minds. Jesus died to give us life. Avoid regularly eating harmful foods or huge portions that could potentially jeopardize our well-being and shorten our time on this earth.

Dear Father,

I am thankful that you sent your son to the earth to be the sacrificial lamb that would pay the price for sin and death and give me eternal life. I am also grateful for the love you show me every day. Please help me love myself and take care of myself.
In Jesus' name,

Amen

Healthy Lifestyle Tip – Eat what you love in moderation, with self-control and a pre-determined food portion. Be careful.

GOD'S MASTERPIECE

Day 44

Ephesians 2:10 (ESV)
For we are his workmanship, created in Christ Jesus for good works,
which God prepared beforehand that we should walk in them.

O ur heavenly Father created us in His image. We are His workmanship, masterpiece, and handiwork. God started with Adam and Eve. Not sure which number of His creation I am, but each of us is God's masterpiece. Some may not like their features or their body type, but in God's eyes, each person is His beautiful masterpiece.

Does the word masterpiece bring to mind other words? Creation, skillful workmanship, or original work, perhaps? The creator God created everyone for His will and good pleasure. Does being overweight, out of balance, and/or unhealthy hinder us from doing God's will? An artist desires to create a masterpiece. Since God is the creator, everyone is His masterpiece. No two pieces of art are exact, and God did not make any of His masterpieces the same.

Masterpieces cost a great deal. Each of us was bought with a great price when Jesus died on Calvary.

How are we taking care of God's masterpiece? Artwork in museums receives special lighting, specific air quality, and regulated temperatures, while also being insured. Who am I? I am God's masterpiece and insured by the blood of the Lamb. Walk in it! Eat and live as one of God's masterpieces. Consistently eat healthy. Occasionally deviating from the plan is acceptable, but be mindful and deliberate about it. Plan and exercise caution, remembering that moderation is crucial.

Dear Lord,

Help me remember I am your masterpiece, created by the master himself! I want to be ready to do your will and fulfill your purpose in my right-sized body. While on the journey to my right-sight body, please help me strive to get there with a plan and execute it daily.
In Jesus' name,

Amen

Healthy Lifestyle Tip – Eat three meals every day. Do not skip meals or starve your body.

LIVING WATER
Day 45

John 6:35
And Jesus said unto them, I am the bread of life: he that cometh to me
shall never hunger; and he that believeth on me shall never thirst.

Samaritan woman met Jesus at the well. He asked her for water, and she gave him a cup. Jesus knew everything about her and told her. She was stunned. As Christians, Jesus is our spiritual thirst quencher, our thirst satisfier. Jesus offered the Samaritan woman living water. Her experience with Jesus baffled her, but she knew she wanted never to thirst again. She was at the well because she was thirsty, but she received more than what she came to the well for.

After her unusual conversation with Jesus, she knew she wanted the Living Water. Jesus told her He could quench her thirst forever. He is the thirst quencher. Our scripture today states that Jesus said to the woman, *He that believeth on me shall never thirst* (John 6:35).

Drink from the fountain; the fountain that never runs dry. Jesus had an encounter with the woman at the well. Have you had an encounter with Jesus?

The Samaritan woman loved everything Jesus was speaking about. She was so excited about meeting the Living Water that she told others, and then they came to the well to meet Jesus.

Keep your physical body hydrated because the body needs and craves water. Hydration aids in the weight loss process. Drink the water! Water will do your body good.

Dear Lord,

Fill my cup, Lord. Reading your Word, praying, and living the Word will keep me spiritually hydrated. Also, help me remember to drink physical water for my body's sake.
In Jesus' name,

Amen

Healthy Lifestyle Tip – Hydrate the body. Drink at least 6-8 eight-ounce glasses of water a day. Some people may require more or less. Ask your doctor.

MY COMMITMENT

Day 46

Psalm 37:5
Commit thy way unto the Lord; trust also in him; and he shall bring it
to pass.

C ommit to the process of healthy eating! Commitment means staying the course, showing up every day, and being consistent. Commit to your eating lifestyle plan, weight loss plan, or diet to the Lord. Tell the Lord your hopes, realistic goals, and dreams. Excess weight will drop if the work is done. If one plan doesn't work because of specific circumstances, try another. Find a program that works for your lifestyle, finances, and your body. Then commit to a program and give it to the Lord with your dedication. Also, talk to your medical professional, dietician, or nutritionist. Trust the process, and the pounds will drop.

It is God's desire for us to be in a relationship with Him in all things. Commune with Him daily. God is concerned about us.

Ready? Set the weight loss plan in motion and go. God be with you until we meet again with less of you. Go with God!

Dear Lord,

> *Oh, Lord, today I commit to my weight loss program, called*
> *_____. (Fill in the blank.)*
> *I want to honor you in my temple and with my eating habits.*
> *In Jesus' name,*
> *Amen.*

Dear Lord,

> *Oh, Lord, today I commit to my new healthy lifestyle, which entails*

> *(Fill in the blank.)*
> *I want to honor you in my temple and with my eating habits.*
> *In Jesus' name,*
>
> *Amen*

Healthy Lifestyle Tip – Review your healthy eating lifestyle plan. Are changes or modifications needed? Recommit today to stay on your weight loss journey.

ENCOURAGE YOURSELF

Day 47

Joshua 1:9 (NIV)
Have I not commanded you? Be strong and courageous. Do not be
afraid; do not be discouraged, for the Lord your God will be with you
wherever you go.

Discouraged? Be strong, courageous, and not afraid. Why? Because God is with us wherever we go. Thanks Joshua! These are empowering words to help us with choosing our foods, exercise regime, and staying on the course. Say these words to yourself. Encourage yourself with the Word of God. Affirmations are nice and have their place in helping us while on this weight loss journey, but the Word of God is powerful and sharper than any two-edged sword.

Use the Word to guide, encourage, and strengthen you during moments of temptations and cravings. Have you ever felt like giving up on doing what is right for your body, God's temple? Share those feelings with the Lord. Which scriptures support and uplift you on your journey? Write these precious verses on 3X5 cards and display them on your bathroom mirror or refrigerator for daily encouragement and inspiration. This practice has worked wonders for me, empowering me and giving me the strength to press onward. So, let's turn that frown upside down, embrace a smile, and find joy in the journey!

Also, ask a friend, mentor, coach, or family member for support and to walk alongside you. What if none are available? Encourage yourself!

Our Gracious Lord and Father,

Sometimes I want to quit because I am discouraged. The journey is hard. I know to put my trust in you, but I falter. Please give me the strength, discipline, and willpower to stay the course. I put my hope and trust in you.
In Jesus' name,

Amen

Healthy Lifestyle Tip – Encourage yourself with words of affirmation.

1. I am working towards living a healthy lifestyle.
2. I'm doing my weight loss journey with God's help.
3. This journey may be difficult, but God is my help!
4. The results of subscribing to the weight loss plan is working for my good.
5. _____
   (Write your own affirmation.)

THE BLOOD

Day 48

1 John 1:7
But if we walk in the light, as he is in the light, we have fellowship one
with another, and the blood of Jesus Christ his Son cleanseth us from
all sin.

W hat is the purpose of blood in our bodies? Blood carries oxygen throughout our bodies. Blood is the lifeline of a living person. The absence of oxygen in the blood means there is no life. Blood testing! A1C levels. The blood in our bodies gives so much data to medical personnel on the condition of our bodies. When medical personnel test or screen our blood, the results can give information about our health dating as far back as three or more months.

When tested, the blood in our bodies provides readings of our blood sugar and cholesterol levels. (The A1C is a blood test used for pre-diabetes or Type 2 diabetes.)

It was necessary for Jesus to shed blood to give us eternal life.

Jesus' shedding of His blood still applies to our lives over 2,000 years later. Jesus had to die to pay the penalty for sin and death because His blood cleanses us from sin.

If we are overweight, with the power of God, exercise, and wise food choices, we can improve the status of our blood numbers. Our aim is to achieve a balanced and healthy weight. Many obese and overweight people must lower their A1C numbers to achieve a healthy status. We do not want to be underweight, overweight, or obese. Let's improve our blood test results through proper nutrition and regular exercise.

Dear Lord,

Oh, the blood that you shed for me on Calvary. Your blood paid the price of sin and death for my eternal life. I thank you, Lord, for your sacrifice. As I eat healthy and exercise, may my blood sugar numbers comply with great health. I can do this with your help.
In Jesus' name,

Amen

Healthy Lifestyle Tip – Add a meatless or plant-based meal to your food plan this week.

WHEN I AM WEAK
Day 49

II Corinthians 12:10
Therefore, I take pleasure in infirmities, in reproaches, in necessities,
in persecutions, in distresses for Christ's sake: for when I am weak,
then am I strong.

O ur scripture reference talks about human weakness, but we can be strong in Jesus Christ. Infirmities! Yes, there are some infirmities that have kept the excess weight on our bodies. There is a plan; hopefully, a written plan will aid in the loss of excess weight.

Experiencing weakness, brokenness, and low self-esteem can show up when one suffers from excess weight on the body. But God! God's strength and power can shine through our weaknesses. Should we take pleasure in being overweight? No, but in our weakness, we can be made strong. We can shed our bodies of excess weight and live a healthier lifestyle. How? Changing bad eating habits and replacing them with good ones is how I will succeed. Be mindful of what foods are going into our mouths and make sure our food portions are adequate. Drinking ample water, getting sufficient rest, and managing stress are also vital components of this journey. Have we heard all of this before?

Well, we take pleasure in that we know our infirmities can turn into strengths as we rely on God's strength. What a beautiful thought to walk in God's strength. When we recognize our need for Him, His power can transform our weaknesses into strengths. When we are weak, then we are strong.

Three antonyms for the word infirmity are healthiness, wholeness, and wellness. Yes, Lord! We want those things! The Lord will turn it around for us, but we must do our part. There is not a fairy godmother waving a wand over our bodies. We must believe God's Word. Do the work. Lean on God and call upon Him. Hold on to His strength.

Dear Lord,

When I am weak, then I am strong. I can do all things with your help and strength. I am helpless without you on this journey with me. I am holding on.
In Jesus' name,

Amen and Amen

Healthy Lifestyle Tip – If you mess up, binge, go off the plan or fall off the wagon, regroup, forgive yourself, and get back on track. Recognize why it happened and make a plan not to let it reoccur.

LACK WISDOM?

Day 50

James 1:5
If any of you lack wisdom, let him ask of God, that giveth to all men
liberally, and upbraideth not; and it shall be given him.

It's been 50 days. Evaluate your progress by reviewing your daily or weekly log of food and exercise sessions. How is the weight loss? Do you need to eliminate certain foods from your plan that are causing weight gain? Use less salt, drink more water, exercise more, add weight training, and possibly do food prep on the weekend. Get knowledge and understanding. Are you getting adequate sleep?

Ask questions. Research. Each of us is unique, and our bodies and lifestyles respond differently to every weight loss program. Check the reviews. So many churches have health initiatives and ministries in the church to teach healthy living, cooking, and eating clean, and many have WW (Weight Watchers) classes.

The Bible says if we lack wisdom, ask God. Remember, God

knows it all. He will direct your steps and pathway. Let Him lead you to the right people concerning our healthy lifestyle and weight loss programs. As stated in the Day 44 devotional, our bodies are unique and masterfully created. Knowledge is power. Find out what works for your body. Ask a medical professional, dietician, or weight loss representative of your weight loss program.

God is mighty in wisdom and strength. Yes, we praise Him for His mighty acts, wisdom, direction, and strength.

Dear Lord God,

You are strong and mighty. You are mighty in wisdom and strength. There is none like you! Thanks for your wisdom and grace in every area of my life. Help me continue to learn, research, and listen to my doctor about what my body needs and how to take care of my temple.
This is my prayer.
In Jesus' name,

Amen

Healthy Lifestyle Tip – Keep a daily log, journal, or progress chart of weight, exercises, and personal thoughts for the day.

HEALS ALL MY DISEASES
Day 51

Psalm 103:3 (NIV)
Who forgives all your sins and heals all your diseases.

Many of us need healing in our minds as we change our negative thoughts to positive ones and healing in our bodies from the abuse of food. We must see ourselves as God sees us, wonderfully made. The temple needs healing.

Many of us need to change our mindset and reprogram our thinking about food. Food is not bad! We need food for nourishment and fuel. However, the problem is what we do with the food. Exercise and portion control are two changes that will aid in the healing of our bodies from the diseases caused by excess weight. If the doctor asks us to refrain from salt, processed, and fried foods to aid in our healing, we must listen and obey.

David, the psalmist, said the Lord will heal our diseases. We must do our part. The Lord has healed and restored many people who changed their ways! When my BMI number went below 30, I was ecstatic with jubilee and praise. I jumped for joy! From obesity to overweight through diet and exercise. I am lowering my risk for diseases, and I feel wonderful. The scale or weight categories do not define us, but we want to be healthy in all things. The journey was long, but I did the work, and I am so happy and blessed. Thank you, Jesus! Next, on to my right-sized body.

David was not talking about the excess weight leaving our bodies through prayer alone. Obesity is a disease. If we follow a food plan and/or change our bad eating habits, those who are obese can heal themselves from the disease of obesity. As we consistently adhere to a weight loss program and/or change our eating habits, the diseases of hypertension (high blood pressure), high cholesterol, heart disease, and Type 2 diabetes might leave our bodies.

Dear Heavenly Father,

I come today to ask you to heal and restore my body. Please bless my efforts, as I am intentionally working on changing my eating habits, watching my food portions, and my thoughts around food and my body. I need thee, oh I need thee. Thanks, dear Father.
In Jesus' name,

Amen

Healthy Lifestyle Tip – Let every diner at the table finish their own food. You are not the clean-up person! Don't eat the food on the plates of others.

IN THE MORNING

Day 52

Psalm 5:3

My voice shalt thou hear in the morning, O Lord; in the morning will I direct my prayer unto thee, and will look up.

As I rise each morning when the sun rises, this signifies a new day and new beginnings. His mercies are new every morning (Ecclesiastes 3:23). Joy comes in the morning also (Psalm 30:5). We can endure the night because the morning is on its way. Trust God because He regulates the morning, noonday, and evening.

We have another day to get it right. Work the food plan, eat the right foods, eat the right portions, exercise, and sleep.

There is research about the benefits of exercising and food planning in the morning. However, get it done whenever you have time to do it.

The sun's job is to light the day and give warmth to the climate, our bodies of water, and the earth. Get some sun while on the weight loss journey. All of us need vitamin D. Our God made the sun and all of its properties and functions on the fourth day of creation (Genesis 1:16). Remember, the sun will shine even if you can't feel its rays. In the morning when I rise, great is God's faithfulness.

Walk in the morning's sunlight. Find a perfect place to pray and read the Bible. Try a prayer walk in the garden or in the park as the morning rays come through the trees. Please protect your skin.

Dear Lord,

In the morning when I rise, you are there. Lord, thank you for another day to work on our plan and live for you. When I go to sleep at night, you are there. I know you are always with me, and I will keep my mind stayed on thee.
In Jesus' name,

Amen

Healthy Lifestyle Tip – Meal prepping ahead of scheduled meals makes cooking meals easier during the week. Try to meal prep on the weekends or on a less busy day to aid in having meals at home.

THE REQUIREMENT
Day 53

John 14:2-3
In my Father's house are many mansions: if it were not so, I would
have told you. I go to prepare a place for you. ³And if I go and prepare
a place for you, I will come again, and receive you unto myself; that
where I am, there ye may be also.

J esus has prepared a place in Heaven for those who have accepted Him as their personal Savior. Thank God there is no weight requirement for entrance into heaven. At the Second Coming, Jesus will supernaturally change our bodies in the middle of the air as we ascend to heaven. There is only one requirement for admittance to heaven; one must have accepted Jesus Christ as their personal Savior.

However, there is a weight requirement to partake in many activities. Such as going on amusement park rides, skydiving, horseback riding, zip-lining, tubing, sitting on chairs, bikes, and using certain exercise equipment. Some outdoor activities state the waist size cannot exceed 45 inches and the thighs cannot exceed 31 inches. Limits, limits, limits. Am I over the limit? Am I going to be measured to qualify to ride? Can I sit on this bench or chair? Will it hold me? Do I meet the weight requirements? What an embarrassment!

Today, there are many programs, tools, strategies, tips, and plans for weight loss. Many are free. They include calorie deficit with exercise, reducing carbohydrate intake, eliminating flour and sugar, counting calories, and weighing and measuring food portions. Lots of proteins, fruit, and vegetables comprise other plans. Whatever the food plan—and there are many more—follow the plan that works for your body and be consistent.

If we eat clean and make healthy food decisions, we will not have to worry about weight requirements after we lose excess weight. More importantly, have you accepted Christ as your personal Savior? [1] Do you meet that requirement? If not, see page 192.

Dear Lord,

Heaven is my final destination for eternity. What joy and happiness I will experience just to be at the feet of Jesus! Thanks for preparing a place for me.
In Jesus' name,

Amen

Healthy Living Tip: Eat high-fiber snacks like carrots, apples, almonds, blueberries, and raspberries to stay full.

SELF-LOVE

Day 54

Psalm 139:14 ESV
I praise you, for I am fearfully and wonderfully made. Wonderful are your works; my soul knows it very well.

Psalm 139:14 reminds us of self-love. I love myself, for I am fearfully and wonderfully made. Who said this? David, the psalmist, wrote this! God tells us in His Word that we are His masterpiece and that He did not make a mistake while creating us. God loves us, and we should love ourselves. Love thyself, but not selfish love. 2 Timothy 3:1-2 (NIV) states, *But mark this: There will be terrible times in the last days. People will be lovers of themselves, lovers of money, boastful, proud, abusive, disobedient to their parents, ungrateful, unholy.* We are not to love ourselves in this manner.

We love the Lord for so many reasons, but do we love ourselves? Note—I did not say love the conditions of our bodies, but do we love ourselves, self-love? Many people cannot look in a mirror or take pictures or put on a bathing suit because they dislike how they look.

We have the power to change and transform our bodies with diet and exercise. The Lord loves us no matter how we look. We should too. However, let's reduce the excess weight of our bodies. It is not healthy.

Do not forget we are fearfully and wonderfully made, and we are God's masterpiece (Ephesians 2:10 NLT)! Let all the people praise Him forever and forever.

Dear Lord,

I love you today with my whole heart. Loving myself is a model for loving others. So, I ask that I would have the mindset to love myself no matter what the scale says and what my body looks like. As I change my mind about eating better and adopting healthy eating habits, I will eat to live healthily. Finally, the strength that you give upholds me and keeps me going. I love you today! Thank you for creating me.
In Jesus' name,

Amen

Healthy Lifestyle Tip – Incorporate protein into your three main meals.

FRIENDS ON THE JOURNEY
Day 55

I Thessalonians 5:11
Wherefore comfort yourselves together, and edify one another, even as
also ye do.

The disciples engaged in ministry, worked, and fished together as a united group. Elisha and Elijah, Naomi and Ruth, Paul, Priscilla, and Aquila, and Paul, Timothy, and Epaphroditus exemplified the strength of friendship and partnership in ministry. So why not embark on your own journey with individuals who will provide encouragement and support? Joining forces with others on the same journey can help motivate and encourage weight loss. They know the struggle. Having a powerful support group is key to staying motivated and committed during your weight loss plan.

Doing a weight loss journey by yourself is doable, but why not with a friend or loved one? While at the gym one day, someone asked if I would join her in a weight loss support group. It scared her to ask because she thought she would offend me. Today, we are best friends. To date, we have lost over 150 pounds together. We talk on the telephone, text, walk, attend weight loss meetings, encourage one another, and subscribe to a weight loss program together.

Many weight loss programs ask or require their participants to call or check in with their sponsor, mentor, or coach when in a food crisis. This can help avoid overeating, binge eating, or going off the food plan for the day or a greater length of time. Joining forces with those on the same path can be a beneficial strategy for achieving weight loss goals and maintaining a healthy lifestyle.

Nothing is wrong with calling a human for help, but our ultimate help is God! *Call to me, and I will answer you, and show you great and mighty things, which you do not know.* (Jeremiah 33:3 NKJV)

Start the day with prayer, entrusting God to start and uphold you on the journey. Find others to join you. An accountability partner helps you stay on track with encouragement, guidance, and friendship.

Dear Lord,

I acknowledge that embarking on a weight loss journey can be challenging and filled with struggles. But I am reminded that I do not have to face these alone. On this weight loss journey, may I trust your guidance and support, and walk alongside others.
In Jesus' name,

Amen

Healthy Lifestyle Tip – Consider having an accountability partner, coach, or mentor during your weight loss, healthy living journey.

IS THIS FOOD FOR ME?

Day 56

I Corinthians 6:12 (ESV)
All things are lawful for me, but not all things are not helpful. "All things are lawful for me," but I will not be dominated by anything.

Certain foods are not suitable for everyone at all times. A Philadelphia cheesesteak sandwich is an amazing food item. (An average cheesesteak is 900 calories, 40 g of fat, 50 g of protein, and 80 g of carbohydrates.) [1] If there is a weight problem, a 900-calorie cheesesteak may not fit into one's diet. A well-rounded diet is necessary. Are others eating a cheesesteak? Others may eat cheesesteaks all the time, but that may not be right for your consumption.

Right now, an authentic Philadelphia cheesesteak may not be on the food plan, but you can make modifications that are permissible. There are creative ways to adapt dishes for weight loss or healthier eating. Research your options. For example, reduce the amount of meat and cheese and place it on Ezekiel bread or low-calorie wrap.

My guilty pleasure is still on my food plan. We eliminated over 300 hundred calories. Thank you, Jesus. I can eat my favorite foods and stay on my healthy weight-loss journey.

Today's scripture says, *All things are lawful unto me, but all things are not expedient: all things are lawful for me, but I will not be brought under the power of any.*

Ask yourself, "Is this food on my food plan?" Decide and make the right choice! Eating should be enjoyable and not a chore to complete. We must eat to live. There are so many references to food in the Bible. Jesus fished, cooked, served the people, and ate. We can too.

For some, eating certain foods can derail a weight loss plan and cause one to backslide or regress on their healthy lifestyle journey. Later, reintroduce foods in moderation. Be careful of your food choices. Choose wisely.

Dear Lord,

Choices. Decisions. Lord, may my mind be true to me, and I wisely choose my foods. When the situation arises, may my hunger levels and cravings allow me to be mindful of my food choices.
In Jesus' name,

Amen

Healthy Lifestyle Tip – Read the food labels. Know the calories and nutritional breakdown of your food. Look for fat, sodium, sugar, and nutritional content.

NEW MERCIES ARE MINE

Day 57

Lamentations 3:22-23
*It is of the L*ORD*'s mercies that we are not consumed, because his compassions fail not. ²³ They are new every morning: great is thy faithfulness.*

Who can grant us mercy? Could it be the teacher who grants mercy when our research paper is not submitted on time, but it is still accepted? Or when we are late to work and not formally reprimanded by our employers? Could it possibly be the traffic court judge when he throws out the charges against us? We could go on and on.

When we go to the doctor and the blood test results state that we do not have one or more of those diseases attributed to obesity, is it because of luck? I think not. It is because of God's mercy. We all want God's mercy. His mercy supersedes all the above and those too many to mention, but the mercy of the Lord frees us a thousand-fold more than any earthly power can.

The title of Margaret Douroux's song "Mercy That Suits" says it all. Mercy suits our case! We can't give ourselves mercy. Someone else must grant it. When we receive mercy, it is not based on anything we have done. God's new mercies come to us each new day. The overwhelming goodness of God is that he grants mercy to the just and unjust, and to the saved and unsaved. His mercies are new every morning. Great is God's faithfulness. (Lamentations 3:22-23)

Let's not rely on God's mercy to not get the diseases that obesity and being overweight have made us at risk for. If we get one or more of those horrible diseases because of our weight issues, we are still here and have not died. Don't dig an early grave. Continue to fight the fat with exercise, drinking water, and continuing to subscribe to a healthy weight loss program.

Dear Lord,

Thank you for the mercy shown to your children. We do not deserve it, but we need your mercy today. Each of us may need mercy for different reasons. We accept your mercy and say thanks.
In Jesus' name,

Amen

Healthy Lifestyle Tip – Choose fresh fruits and vegetables. Farm to Table. It is advisable to grow some of your food if you can.

(Even in some cities, farms bring their produce to the city on a weekly basis all year-long.)

ALL THINGS POSSIBLE

Day 58

Matthew 19:26 (NIV)
Jesus looked at them and said, "With man this is impossible, but with
God all things are possible."

Losing weight is not an easy feat for many. Sticking to a healthy lifestyle takes discipline and commitment. Advertisements, family dinners, parties, and bakeries make food choices very difficult, but God is our help. Jesus said the words, *"With man, this is impossible, but with God, all things are possible.*

Weight loss is achievable. Embrace a healthy lifestyle! With God, all things are possible, that includes weight loss. "With God" is the most important phrase of that verse. However, the journey requires effort on our part. There are no magic wands to make the weight vanish instantly. God can help us stay on course, make the right food choices, and exercise!

At times, you may not want to follow the plan, but with God's help, it becomes achievable. Our impossibilities are God's possibilities. Losing five pounds is not an insurmountable feat, but shedding 100 pounds can feel monumental. Yes, there are many people that don't have to do a weight loss journey but remember, this is the journey prescribed for us. This journey has benefits. Each loss pound will add up and contribute to the journey's success.

Surround yourself with people who are also trying to lose weight for motivation and support. Look for like-minded people in your church, neighborhood, online forums, Facebook groups, or among friends. Draw inspiration from real-life success stories showcased in magazines, books, YouTube, and television shows. Know that weight loss is achievable and within your reach. With God, all things are possible. To achieve weight loss, make changes to your diet, eat fewer calories, and develop healthy eating habits. I've tried each one of these and they truly work!

Dear Lord,

Sometimes this journey seems impossible. Help me, Lord, to remember that with you all things are possible. When the road gets long and dreary and I can't see the end of the tunnel, please give me the understanding that all things are possible with you. So thankful for your help, wisdom, and encouragement from the Word of God.
In Jesus' name,

Amen

Healthy Lifestyle Tip – Refrain from drinking your calories.

HUMBLE ME

Day 59

James 4:10 (NIV)
Humble yourselves before the Lord, and he will lift you up.

B e humble! Now that you've lost some, most, or all of the excess weight, do not look down on others or body shame those who have not lost their weight. Our scripture states to humble ourselves. Our weight loss should not puff us up with pride. Be careful, because pride might puff up our shrunken fat cells. Pride goes before a fall. Pride is a sin. In Proverbs 11:12, the Bible says, *When pride comes, then comes disgrace, but with the humble is wisdom.*

Losing weight, looking good, and feeling amazing in your body after weight loss is a personality booster. But don't look down on other people who continue to struggle with their weight, can't stay on course, or do not have the mindset to lose weight. For some who lose weight, their footsteps are lighter and they feel lighter. Some find a new level of self-esteem, but Lord, keep me humble.

Consider praying for others struggling on their healthy eating journey.

Looking back over your journey of weight loss, the changes you made to your diet have made a difference. I love how my body looks and feels. (Lord, please keep me humble.) The fat cells are still in me, just shrunken. I don't want pride to overtake me, nor do I want to eat the wrong foods, reclaim bad eating habits, and stop exercising. This behavior will re-energize my fat cells. Lord, please help me maintain my weight loss and not re-energize my fat cells.

Look how far you've come. Let your data (weigh-in numbers) humble you. You did it! Where do you go from here? Maintain your healthy weight by not revisiting old eating habits. The same God that walked with you during the weight loss journey will keep you during the maintenance phase. Want to be kept? Want to live wonderfully in your new body? Do not bring the excess weight back. Continue your healthy lifestyle changes.

Dear Lord,

Keep me day by day. Help me not to judge others who are struggling with their weight and journey! Help them, Lord. Humble me, Lord, and help me remain on course all the way to the end, which is my right-sized body forever.
In Jesus' name,

Amen

Healthy Lifestyle Tip – Eliminate saturated and trans fats (bad fats) from your food plan. Choose healthy ones like monounsaturated and polyunsaturated fats, which can be found in olive oil, avocados, and walnuts.

VICTORY IS MINE

Day 60

1 Corinthians 15:57 (NIV)
*But thanks be to God, who gives us the victory through our Lord Jesus
Christ.*

Almost everyone wants to be a winner. Broad smiles happen
on the scale when weight loss has been achieved. Did you
lose one ounce, one pound, five pounds, or ten pounds?
Celebrate each victory, great or small. Give a shout of praise to God
for all completed achievements and goals. We are victorious!

Help! When in trouble, Jesus told us to call on Him and He will
answer and show up (Jeremiah 33:3). In our food battle, Jesus is the
captain of our team. He will fight the battle for us. What are the
plans and strategies for losing weight? Write them and make them
plain. The battle is over. We win! Romans 6:37 states, *Nay, in all
these things we are more than conquerors through him that loved us,*
but we must know the plan and follow it. The plan must be doable,
make sense, and be sustainable.

Nonetheless, our flesh sometimes gets weary, and we get scared we will fail and regress. For many reading this devotional, this is not the first-time dieting or choosing a healthy weight loss plan.

All achievements are worth celebrating. It's midnight, and I did not eat a half gallon of chocolate ice cream before bed. Yes! Congratulations to me. I did not overeat at tonight's meal. Yes! Victory is mine. Victory is not losing excess pounds. Victory is overcoming the daily food challenges. The result is weight loss.

Celebrate every win, but please don't celebrate with the foods that have derailed your progress in the past. Celebrate with non-food rewards. Jesus has already won it for us. Shout now! You may get weary, but do not give up. Many victories come after previous failures. Correct negative behaviors without speaking negative thoughts about yourself. Victory today is mine. Walk in victory!

Dear Lord,

I am a victor in Christ Jesus. The battle and struggle of losing weight and sticking to it belongs to you. I rely on you! Help me when I get scared and encourage me when I fail. Please remind me when I forget that the battle is yours. Victory is mine today.
In Jesus' name,

Amen

Healthy Lifestyle Tip – Eliminate white refined all-purpose flour. Consider replacing white refined flour with chickpea flour, almond flour, rice flour, oat flour, or buckwheat flour.

WITHOUT MURMURINGS and COMPLAINING

Day 61

Philippians 2:14
Do all things without murmurings and disputings:

To murmur is to complain in a low tone or in private.[1] God hears everything we say. We can blame others for our weight problems and reasons for overeating, but we must take ownership of what goes into our mouths. Temptation around food is at every corner, even when pumping gas. A video about the food that is available inside the store plays as soon as you activate the gas pump. Fast-food restaurants are often linked to gas stations. Pump the gas and then buy the fast food. What about the food samples in supermarkets or department stores? Does your hand reach for the free tastings without thought?

Do not play the blame game. Our lifestyle comprises eating three meals (or six small meals) a day, but food choices and portion control are the keys to weight loss. These temptations are not going away.

For more than 30 years, I attributed my excess weight to having babies, then I realized how unreasonable that belief was. I had to take ownership of my bad eating habits and large portions. Stop murmuring and blaming others, stay on the plan, exercise the body, exercise self-control, and feel the weight drop! But how do we shine while on the weight journey? We can do this.

We shine by the pounds dropping, changing our diet, consistently making great food choices, and showing up for ourselves. Our path may bring others to start the same type of journey. Find the joy in the journey.

Dear Lord,

I apologize for blaming others for my excess weight and complaining about my dietary restrictions. I apologize for not seeing the bigger picture of how making small food changes will change my temple for the better. May I inspire others to know this change is achievable.
In Jesus' name,

Amen

Healthier Lifestyle Tip – Make at least 2-3 changes in your bad eating habits. As long as you do not eat more calories, a minor change will reap enormous benefits to your body/health.

MY NEW BODY

Day 62

2 Corinthians 5:17
Therefore, if any man be in Christ, he is a new creature: old things are
passed away; behold, all things are become new.

When you hear the word *new*, what comes to mind? Perhaps new walk, new wine (Matthew 9:16), new eyes, new life or creature, new song (Psalm 40:3), new things (Isaiah 43:19), new name (Isaiah 62:2 or Revelation 2:17), new heaven and new earth (Isaiah 65:17), new spirit and new heart (Ezekiel 36:26), new clothes (Matthew 9:17), and new covenant (Hebrews 12:24).

The Bible ends with Revelation 21:5, *And he that sat upon the throne said, Behold, I make all things new. And he said unto me, Write: for these words are true and faithful.* Put away the old and take on the new. Jesus makes us brand new!

What about our new body? Our body is daily being transformed as we eat healthy foods in proper portions. As we stick to a healthy weight loss program, our bodies will change. Review old pictures of when your weight was out of control. Document the journey. No need to show everyone those pictures unless you want to. Let the new pictures and the data from your weigh-ins be the documentation for your testimony and guide for continued success or how to pivot to get to the success of weight loss.

After the excess weight loss, what will I look like and how will I feel in my new body? Imagine it. There is a computer program application (app) called *Envisionbody*. The digital app shows the new you after weight loss in real-time. (No endorsement here!) Digital pictures of you with future weight loss could be a real motivator.

Experiencing life in my new body is an incredible sensation. Even though my weight loss journey is not complete, I absolutely adore my transformed physique. Carrying 80 excess pounds seems absurd to me now, yet I did it for years. Today, running up and down the tennis courts does not require numerous water breaks; they were more like rest breaks. Climbing up a flight of stairs with such ease fills me with exhilaration.

Saints of God, pray and ask God to help you with the transformation of your mind and body while staying the course.

Dear Lord,

You make all things brand new. No one has that power but you. I want to put off the old and put on the new. I want to do new things in my life. My reliance is on you for help and strength in this area.
In Jesus' name,
Amen

Healthy Lifestyle Tip – Start your day early. Read your Bible, exercise, and eat breakfast.

THE FOOD TEST

Day 63

Daniel 1:15
And at the end of ten days their countenances appeared fairer and
fatter in flesh than all the children which did eat the portion of the
king's meat.

The Bible does not state that Daniel had a weight problem, but it does state he was in a spiritual dilemma with his three Hebrew friends—Shadrach, Meshach, and Abednego. Daniel and his three friends decided not to eat King Nebuchadnezzar's food or his fine wine. Can you imagine being given the opportunity to eat the highest quality of food and drink the wine prepared for the king and you? Remember, there were all the others that were in training too who were eating the bountiful feast every day for three years (Daniel 1).

Daniel and his friends decided not to eat the king's meat and wine. They requested of the king that they only eat vegetables and water for 10 days to prove to him that their bodies and mind would be fit and fine for service. Ten days later, they proved just that.

Daniel, Shadrach, Meshach, and Abednego exhibited commitment, discipline, self-control, and willpower. Did they sit at the table with the others while the others ate King Nebuchadnezzar's food? Not sure, but we know they did not eat the king's food or drink the wine. May we exhibit that same self-control and commitment as we walk our weight loss journey. The three Hebrew boys and Daniel had a food plan and stuck to it! Were they tempted to eat the king's food? Not sure, but they had access to the king's food and wine and did not partake! They knew the expected outcome and results they wanted. Eating the king's food would not get those results. Daniel, Shadrach, Meshach, and Abednego achieved significant results in their subscribed food plan. The king was thrilled and elevated them.

Commitment, discipline, and self-control are ours today.

Dear Lord,

Please help me have the same type of commitment and discipline that Daniel, Shadrach, Meshach, and Abednego possessed. Help me stick to my food plan and commitment to living a healthy lifestyle. Thank you,
Jesus.
In Jesus' name,

Amen

Healthy Living Tip – Try the Daniel Fast for one meal per week or for an entire month to three months. Also, consider eating at least 3-5 servings of vegetables every day.

THAT'S LOVE

Day 64

Romans 5:8 (NKJV)
But God demonstrates His own love towards us, in that while we were
still sinners, Christ died for us.

God sent his son Jesus to the earth to die for each of us to give us eternal life. Jesus paid it all on the cross. He bore all our iniquities, sin, and shame.

How can we repay Him for all He has done and continues to do for us? We really cannot repay Him because the cost is too high. However, we can take care of the bodies He gave us, serve Him, and glorify Him. I Corinthians 6:20 states we are to glorify the Lord in our bodies.

God loves us! He loves us even with all the excess weight we carry around. It's not worth the weight. Love yourself. Love you! Love the excess weight? I think not. Would He send His Son to die for us if it had not been for love? The Father loves us. Remember, *But God demonstrates His own love towards us, in that while we were still sinners, Christ died for us.* (Romans 5:8 NJKV) God's love is shown to us continuously, and it never runs dry.

Your body relies on you to nurture and cherish it. Show it the respect it deserves. Scriptures and uplifting affirmations can help during a challenging lifestyle journey. Reach out to a friend who is also on a similar journey for encouragement and support. Personally, I am immensely grateful for my walking buddies, past and present; their love and encouragement have been a true blessing. Being part of a weight loss community has been incredibly valuable. We connect through phone calls and texts, providing each other with unwavering support and motivation. Together, we lift and inspire one another along this transformative journey.

Do you feel the love of Jesus Christ? He has shown His love towards us on a daily basis. Love yourself enough to stay on this weight loss journey. Do not give up!

Dear Lord,

Oh, such love that was shown to us on Calvary. I cannot repay you for what you've done for me. Taking care of my body and focusing on eating healthy is my desire. I give you glory, honor, and praise!
In Jesus' name,

Amen

Healthy Lifestyle Tip – Is your body screaming for fiber and nutritious food? Try an unfamiliar vegetable or fruit.

IS LIFE MORE THAN FOOD?

Day 65

Matthew 6:25 (NIV)
Therefore I tell you, do not worry about your life, what you will eat or drink; or about your body, what you will wear. Is not life more than food, and the body more than clothes?

The key phrase from today's scripture reference is, *"Is not life more than food?"* Some of us may find that food holds greater importance than life itself. Consuming excessive amounts of fried, processed, hydrogenated fatty foods, sugary drinks, and alcohol can contribute to various diseases that are associated with obesity and lead us to a life of poor health!

So, is not life more than food? Life is more important than food or drink! Living our life in Christ is our ultimate goal. God will provide for us in all things and will take care of us. Some of us live to eat! Although food is necessary to fuel the body, we should not allow it to consume our thoughts. Unlike animals, they do not worry about it.

Before the start of the day, it is advisable to devise a food plan for the day. By completing a food plan for the day beforehand, you have already eliminated the worry over what to eat at mealtime. Difficulties arise when food plans must be changed or our cravings ask us to change the food plan for the day. It is not a sin to make changes to the plan, but try not to do this consistently.

So, is not life more than food? The Bible says it is.

While on a food plan, be accountable to yourself. Stay committed to the journey and put in the effort. Significant results will follow. Worry not about what you eat or drink. How is your life in Christ? Every time you eat, choose life. Choose a healthy lifestyle. Choose to live and not die. We have a choice! Please choose wisely.

Dear Lord,

I am so sorry for my poor food choices in the past. I now choose life over food. Please help me not to let food control and lead my life. I choose to stay on the healthy lifestyle journey in my thoughts, while shopping in the supermarket, going through the fast-food drive-through, and at mealtimes. I'm so happy to be kind to my temple! Thank you, Jesus.
In Jesus' name,

Amen

Healthy Lifestyle Tip – Avoid processed foods and fast-food restaurants.

THE DESIRES OF THE FLESH

DAY 66

Galatians 5:16 (ESV)
But I say, walk by the Spirit, and you will not gratify the desires of the
flesh.

The flesh wants what it wants when it wants. The scripture says to walk in the Spirit and we will not gratify the desires of the flesh. This is very difficult without walking in the power of the Holy Spirit and totally relying on Him. I never heard a message or sermon about food with our scripture reference mentioned together, but I will make the connection now. The purpose of food is to give us nourishment and fuel. However, eating three hamburgers at a picnic or in the car after visiting a fast-food restaurant is overeating, and the calories not burned will be stored in the body as fat. There is nothing wrong with the beef or turkey in the hamburger, but three in one meal? Self-control is one of the fruits of the spirit.

It is a known fact that people eat with their eyes first. Food plating is an art form. Chefs beautifully plate with colors, textures, and well-cooked food to please the eye and then the palate of the customer.

Eating what we want, when we want, and how much we want can be a heavy weight, and I don't just mean the extra pounds, either. We must crucify the flesh when we want to overeat.

Eat, plan, order, and cook your food under the guidance of the Holy Spirit. This may seem ludicrous, but if someone has a problem in this area, they must listen to their body and rely on the Holy Spirit to know when to stop eating. A food addict does not differ from a sex addict. Something controls an addict. This seems harsh, but abusing food and having a lack of self-control around food can and will harm our bodies, the temples God gave us. This may be too extreme for some, but if extreme overeating is your problem, give this problem to God. Some of us also might need to seek professional help as well.

Dear God,

What a blessing it is to eat great food. May I eat in moderation and eat foods that will not make me gain excess weight, clog my arteries and organs, and put me at risk for specific diseases. I want to live in a healthy body!
In Jesus' name,

Amen

Healthy Lifestyle Tip – Overeating vegetables, fruits and lean proteins can create excess weight in our bodies. Portion control is key.

I SEE YOU

Day 67

II Corinthians 12:11 (NIV)
I have made a fool of myself, but you drove me to it. I ought to have been commended by you, for I am not in the least inferior to the 'super-apostles,' even though I am nothing.

In Hebrews, Paul speaks about being a nobody. After all his work among the people, people still thought he was a nobody. Sometimes people see us as nobodies as well. People often see our body size before they see us, the person. But God sees us as someone! Although we have excess weight on our bodies, we are still valued and have great worth. It is not what people say about us. It is what we say about ourselves. Although Paul was not validated by the people whom he served, Paul knew he was somebody. Paul showed humility.

Sometimes we do not value ourselves. Our weight loss/healthy eating journey may have had ups and downs, victories of losing pounds, and failures of gaining pounds. Does anyone really know how we feel except Jesus? He knows our weaknesses. Others may have had similar feelings and experiences, but God knows how we feel. Our feelings touch him.

Each of us is precious in His sight and is special to Him. Would God send his son to earth for nobodies? Absolutely not! God sent His son to die for us because He loves us and we are special in His sight.

In a crowd of 1,500 or in a group of ten, it is likely people do not see us. God sees, knows, and hears us. We matter in His sight. Sometimes people only see our size and make judgments about us. Not God! God sees us!

Be encouraged. Know that you are seen and special to God.

But you, beloved, building yourselves up on your most holy faith, praying in the Holy Spirit, ²¹keep yourselves in the love of God, looking for the mercy of our Lord Jesus Christ unto eternal life. Jude 20-21

Dear Lord,

So glad I am seen by you. Great to know that my weaknesses touch you and you know them one by one. Lord, only you! Grateful! I am so grateful.
In Jesus' name,

Amen

Healthy Lifestyle Tip – Self-care! Self-care might help reduce stress in our lives or provide a break from it. Take care of yourself! Stress loves to hold on to excess fat. Let it go!

A TESTIMONY

Day 68

Luke 21:13
And it shall turn to you for a testimony.

Psalm 119:31 (ESV)
I cling to your testimonies, O Lord, let me not be put to shame.

We can find the word "test" in the first four letters of the word "testimony." A weight loss journey is a test of our commitment, drive, discipline, and willpower. The major component is that Jesus walks with us and aids us as we walk this journey. We have help, supernatural help.

During tests, cravings, and challenges, we must make good choices. Be ready to handle food challenges and decisions when those challenges arise. What will you say to yourself when these challenges, cravings, and temptations arise?

"Is this dish going to help me reach the healthier me?"

"Will this 'cheat' food item derail me for weeks to come?"

"Can I just have one or two cookies and not 25 of them?"

Eating and making food choices are a daily occurrence. No matter what the circumstance, there will be unhealthy cravings, challenges, and food decisions to test our resolve. These challenges allow us to assess if we have the strength to do what is right for our bodies. Make the right choice. Continue to ask yourself these questions. Will this food choice help me get to my goal weight? Is this food choice aligned with my food plan? Will this food choice hurt, harm, or give nutritional value to my body? Do not be afraid. Be ready for the test! Program your mind for healthy choices. Our bodies will thank us.

Consider reading testimonies of those who successfully made a change and have transformed their bodies and health.,

Dear Lord,

I want to live with a healthy body. My life, actions, and food choices must be a living testimony to the God I worship and adore. I want to glorify you in all that I do. This is my prayer today.
In Jesus' name,

Amen

Healthy Lifestyle Tip – For emergencies, keep healthy snacks at home, work, or in your car. Examples: pre-packaged nuts, carrots, and low-fat pretzels.

I WILL RESTORE

Day 69

Jeremiah 30:17 (NIV)
But I will restore you to health and heal your wounds, declares the
LORD, because you are called an outcast, Zion for whom no one cares.

I will restore, declares the Lord! Do you need healing and restoration of health in your body? Pray and ask God for healing. Jehovah Rapha, the God that heals. However, we must do what is humanly possible on our part. God does the miraculous, but we must eat right, exercise, and show discipline. If we lack any of these, pray and ask God for help. We must not ask God for the healing of our bodies while continuing to eat unhealthy foods and large portions and/or binge eat. Eating processed and fast foods every day will not heal the body, either. I can purchase a salad at the drive-through, you say. Yes, you can, but what about the heavy-laden with calories, fatty salad dressing, and added toppings? Some salad dressings contain sugar, salt, and loads of calories. Read the label and/or research the nutritional value.

Choose this day to eat clean and eat proper portions. Choose to treat your body with the ingredients and foods that will make the body whole. Our food choices might prevent some diseases. Please make correct food choices. Ask your health professionals for help with decision-making around food.

There will be days when caution is thrown to the wind. Get back on the plan for the very next meal or day. Do not wait until the start of a new week, month, or year. Did Daniel and his three friends in the Old Testament have any cravings for the King's food? The Bible doesn't mention if they did. However, Daniel and his friends were focused on presenting their bodies fit and healthy while on their own God-prescribed food plan.

Dear Lord,

As I eat and live a healthy lifestyle, please restore my body to wellness. My food choices will honor my temple and lead me to great health. In Jesus' name,

Amen

Healthy Lifestyle Tip – Make your own healthy salad dressing or vinaigrette.

Marlene's Lemon - Mustard Vinaigrette
   (See page 185 for the recipe.)

DISCOURAGED?

Day 70

John 14:27
Peace I leave with you, my peace I give unto you: not as the world
giveth, give I unto you. Let not your heart be troubled, neither let it be
afraid.

I n the Bible, Elisha, Moses, Sarah, David, and others experienced moments of discouragement. They had to learn to rely on and trust God to see them through their difficulties. In Luke 18:1, Luke writes, *Then Jesus told his disciples a parable to show them they should always pray and not give up.* Take Luke's advice. Pray and don't give up. When discouragement comes, pray. Tell God all about it. Cast your burdens upon the Lord (Psalm 55:22).

Trying to lose weight and stay on a healthy lifestyle plan can be difficult when your mind says one thing, your stomach another, and your nutritious food plan something completely different. At every turn, food and snack ads bombard us. Family and friends encourage us to eat and drink things that are not good for us. And then we have our own unhealthy cravings for food and drink. Help us, Lord!

The numbers on the scale went in the wrong direction this week, but I stayed on the food plan and did not cheat. Although I exercised, I still gained. Water retention, lack of sleep, eating less than 2-3 hours before bed, stress, and other factors can make the numbers on the weight scale rise. Do not give up. Sometimes the scale does not report all the work that has been done, but the body knows. The numbers will eventually go down.

Are you discouraged? Your right-sized body will come one meal and one day at a time. Hope in the Lord, make small changes, and choose a weight loss plan that is sustainable. Remember, *I can do all things through Christ that strengthens me* (Philippians 4:13). Ask the Savior for help! Focus on eating healthy and not the number on the body weight scale. Review your food plan and make the necessary changes to stay the course.

Don't give up! Encouragement is yours today. See yourself in your transformed body because of healthy food choices. You got this!

Dear Lord,

Encourage my soul today. With your help, I can eat right and choose delicious foods that are healthy. I praise you, O Lord, my encourager.
Thank you, Lord.
In Jesus' name,

Amen

Healthy Lifestyle Tip – Stay on the journey! The journey is one meal and one day at a time.

MY HOPE

Day 71

Psalm 31:24
Be of good courage, and he shall strengthen your heart, all ye that hope
in the Lord.

Why is it sometimes difficult for us to put our hope and trust in God and choose to put it in earthen vessels? When do we lose hope? Can I really lose 15, 40, 100, or even 150 pounds? Do we lose hope when our dream dies, when we fail over and over, or when our expectations are not met? We have been on this healthy lifestyle journey for a while, but don't lose hope during the journey. Visualize yourself at the finish line, accepting the trophy of success of excess weight leaving your body.

When the road and journey look bleak, keep your hand in God's hand. Ask Him to help you when your faith and hope waver. He will strengthen and keep you because He can do it. Psalm 31:4 states, *Be of good courage, and he shall strengthen your heart, all ye that hope in the Lord.* Friends, family members, and others want to help and mean well with their platitudes, suggestions, and words of encouragement about eating, our selection of foods, and fitness, but remember, God knows and has plans for you. (Jeremiah 29:11)

Putting all your hopes solely in a diet or weight loss program can lead to disappointment and frustration. Some expectations, results, and outcomes are not always achieved due to many circumstances. To actively show up and adhere to the program is essential for success. Instead, put your ultimate hope in God to guide you through the process and empower you to change your eating habits.

He sees the bigger picture and will light your path. As you do the work, the pounds will drop off as we do the work. Surrender your dreams, desires, food struggles, and expectations to Him. Psalm 31:24 NLT encourages us, *"So cheer up! Take courage if you are depending on the Lord."* There is hope; hope in the Lord!

Lord,

Please strengthen me. I struggle with my weight issues. My hope is in you because there is no other. I am so glad you care about me in every facet of my life. I love you, Lord.
In Jesus' name,

Amen

Healthy Lifestyle Tip – Mindful eating at all meals! Be mindful and present while eating a meal. Know what's going in your mouth.

MY WORDS HAVE POWER
Day 72

Proverbs 18:21 (NIV)
The tongue has the power of life and death, and those who love it will eat its fruit.

O ur words have power! Be careful of the words that leave the mouth. King Solomon wrote these words. He said, "The tongue has the power of life and death." Saying, "I am a fatty!" does not edify the Lord our God, who supports us on the weight loss journey. Speak of those things that please God. If we call ourselves terrible names, the self-fulfilling prophecy can and will go into effect. "I'll never lose weight!" Are those words true? Do I really want that to happen? Are we sabotaging our progress with our words? When feeling challenged in this way, say, *I can do all things through Christ that strengthens me* (Philippians 4:13), or, *I am the righteousness of God!* (2 Corinthians 5:21).

Death and life are in the tongue. Do not speak negative or hurtful words or thoughts to yourself or to others. Hurtful words are destructive and do damage. Since we need much help on this journey, do not kill the weight loss journey with your words. Tell yourself, "I will build up, not tear down—either myself or others—with my words."

The tongue has the power—to kill and destroy. That same tongue also tastes the food that we eat. The tongue is involved in what we speak and put into our stomachs. Be kind to yourself with your words and actions.

Foods that are fried, processed, and contain hydrogenated fats can slowly harm our bodies. This will not happen immediately but over time. Some diseases, physical ailments, and clogged arteries result from those foods, eaten over time. Be mindful of the words your tongue utters and what foods you lay on it.

Dear God, our Father,

The Word of God says the tongue is sharper than a two-edged sword. May my words bless you, me, and others. I need help with what comes out of my mouth and what foods I put on my tongue. Thank you, Jesus, in advance.
In Jesus' name,

Amen

Healthy Lifestyle Tip – As much as possible, eat home-cooked meals with controlled portions.

IS ANYTHING TOO HARD?

Day 73

Jeremiah 32:27
Behold, I am the Lord, the God of all flesh: is there any thing too hard
for me?

Is there an overweight issue or the need to reduce excess weight
to lower one's A1C levels (a blood test for Type 2 diabetes and
pre-diabetes)? Has carrying excess weight on your body led to
weight-related diseases? Is it too difficult for God to assist me in
lowering my disease risk? Nothing is too hard for God. It may be
challenging for us, but not for God. My help is in the Lord who made
heaven and earth. He will help us with the diet plan and staying on
track. Start each day with prayer and ask God for His wisdom in
making daily food choices.

We can win! We can do anything with the help of the Lord! Is
there anything in life just too hard or difficult to achieve? No! Weight
loss and following a food plan can be on the list for some, but our God
is there is help us follow it! Nothing is too hard for Him. God is

omniscient (all-knowing), omnipotent (all-powerful), and omnipresent (present everywhere). God has it all under control.

There is nothing too hard for God. God has the power to aid anyone who asks for help in a weight loss journey. Trying to change your life by eating clean is no problem for God.

With determination and discipline, I successfully shed 81.5 pounds with a food plan and a mentor. I am determined not to regain the excess weight. Adopting new eating habits can be challenging. I find solace in that nothing is too difficult for God. While it might seem hard for me, I will rely on His strength to carry sustain me on this journey.

Nothing is too hard for God. Need self-control while eating? God is there. We often refuse His help because the flesh wants what it wants. Continue to remember that our God can do anything but fail. Even if the circumstances (having to lose over 50 or 100 pounds) seem insurmountable; God is here to help. We fail; God never fails. Watch Him work out His plan and promises in our lives. See and experience His power! Go with God and with His help!

Dear Heavenly Father,

My confidence is in you. With your power, strength, and guidance, I can do anything. But in the moments when the journey gets tough, please remind me I must always rely on you. For in you I live, move, and have my being. Thanks for being my greatest supporter.
In Jesus' name,
Amen

Healthy Lifestyle Tip – Seek, pray, and ask God for help with making the right choices for healthy eating. Then use His encouragement!

GOD, THE SUPPLIER

Day 74

Philippians 4:19
But my God shall supply all your need according to his riches in glory
by Christ Jesus.

His Word states God will supply all our needs. The key word is *need*. Although we receive some of our wants, the scripture reference doesn't say He will supply all our wants. Deep-fried duck-fat fried chicken and French fries sound delicious, but they are not suitable for this journey. (One option is to spray the chicken and French fries with duck fat oil spray and place them into the Air Fryer.) However, our heavenly Father gives us some of our wants, a lobster salad with minimal mayonnaise. We can live without our wants, but indulging in unhealthy eating can kill us or have us at risk for some diseases. Later, we can reintroduce some foods back into our diet. Moderation is key.

There are many scriptures about food in the Bible. Jesus fed the 5000-plus people with five loaves of bread and two fishes. Jesus taught the disciples how to fish for food and then cooked it for them on the beach. God fed Elisha with a cake (not with our white, refined, bleached, all-purpose flour) when he ran from Jezebel. "Won't He do it?" What do we need today from the Lord? Can you remember how God supplied your physical needs in the past? Jehovah Jireh, God provides!

Be mindful. Do we really need four chocolate candy bars just because they are on sale near the cash register? Evaluating your needs versus wants. What food fuel does my body need? What cravings do I have that my body wants in my mouth and stomach? Am I really hungry?

Dear Lord,

I bless you today. With a humble heart, I am grateful for the many blessings given to me and my family. Thanks for the food that I can purchase. I recognize everyone cannot purchase quality food where I live or around the world. Thanks for supplying all of my needs.
In Jesus' name,

Amen

Healthy Lifestyle Tip – Since we eat with our eyes first, remember to cook flavorful, healthy meals containing ingredients of many colors on the plate.

JESUS, THE CHEF
Day 75

John 21:9, 12&13 (NIV)
When they landed, they saw a fire of burning coals there with fish on it,
and some bread. ¹²Jesus said to them, "Come and have breakfast."
None of the disciples dared ask him, "Who are you?" They knew it was
the Lord. ¹³Jesus came, took the bread and gave it to them, and did the
same with the fish.

Come and dine! The Master is calling. Have you ever had breakfast at the Sea of Galilee? The disciples did. One morning at daybreak, the disciples saw Jesus on the seashore cooking. Jesus taught many lessons that morning. Jesus taught the disciples how to fish. He cooked the fish and fed them fish and bread. Jesus met their need to learn the skill of fishing, met their physical hunger need with fish and bread, and met their spiritual need by showing them how to fish for souls. The Master teacher demonstrated what it meant to be a servant and how to follow Him. Jesus, the Master teacher!

If we had a personal chef serving us healthy meals each day, maybe this weight loss or lifestyle journey would be easier. If we had Jesus preparing fish for us as He did for the disciples, this weight loss process would be easier. Jesus is not coming to earth to cook for us and a personal chef daily cooking our meals may not be an option. Jesus has equipped us with His Word, however, and will give us strength to help us on this journey. Tap into it.

There are many cookbooks, as well as easy recipes in magazines and on the internet, to help with healthy flavorful foods. Find flavorful, quick, and easy recipes that align with your weight loss food plan. I'm not sure how much time it took Jesus to cook the fish for the disciples, but I can't believe it was very long. For us, grilling, broiling, and cooking fish in a cast iron pan or Air Fryer is a quick way to prepare an easy protein. If you don't have time to cook, think of the aforementioned ways of preparing fish. (Buy the fish cleaned.) Once again, purchase, cook, and eat healthy foods for weight loss!

Dear Lord,

In your Word, you've fed the disciples and multitudes with food, met the physical needs of the people, and then met their spiritual needs. Thanks for doing the same for me today. My Jehovah Jireh! My provider! I worship and adore you.
In Jesus' name,

Amen

Healthy Lifestyle Tip – Choose to start your day with a healthy breakfast. Jesus fixed breakfast for the disciples.

HAVING THE MIND OF CHRIST

Day 76

I Corinthians 2:16 (NIV)
Who has known the mind of the Lord so as to instruct him? But we
have the mind of Christ.

Our minds often deceive us and give us the wrong narrative. "I'll never lose weight," "My body will always be fat," and so on. We must redirect and retrain our minds and say what Jesus says about us. When we accept Christ as our Savior, we receive the mind of Christ. Speak what Christ says from the Bible. Speak the Word aloud. Write it on paper and in your hearts. Redirect bad thoughts, incorrect thinking, and negativity into positive thoughts and words. When the negative thoughts come, have your positive rebuttal ready. Write your negative thoughts and then rewrite the words into positive thoughts in a journal. Reprogram your mind.

A weight loss journey is a major undertaking. Many dieters experience the cycle of starting and stopping, yo-yo dieting with fluctuating weight, while others eventually give up altogether. Our mindset must be ready to take care of ourselves through weight loss. Eating right, exercising, proper sleep, and correct portions are great, but if your mind is not right, it will sabotage the weight loss and derail the journey. Sometimes we tell ourselves information that is not true or we let others speak negativity into our lives. Remember, we have the mind of Christ. Look at life through the eyes of Jesus and His Word. What would Jesus say? Jesus would never put us down. We are God's creation.

Philippians 4:8 says, *Finally, brethren, whatsoever things are true, whatsoever things are honest, whatsoever things are just, whatsoever things are pure, whatsoever things are lovely, whatsoever things are of good report; if there be any virtue, and if there be any praise, think on these things.* We have the mind of Christ!

Dear Father,

Let the words of my mouth and the meditations of my heart be acceptable unto you, dear Lord. Please help me as I reprogram my mind and have the mind of Christ. Let me speak words of truth. Glory to your name!
In Jesus' name,

Amen

Healthy Lifestyle Tip – Read, write, meditate, speak, and memorize those verses that will encourage you on this journey.

SATISFY HIM

Day 77

Psalm 91:16
"With long life will I satisfy him, and shew him my salvation."

Jesus satisfies. He quenches our thirst for living water. He satisfies our needs and gives us a sense of belonging, as we are His children. Jesus gives us the assurance that we will meet Him in Heaven for eternity. Our souls yearn for someone who can satisfy us, and His name is Jesus! But our body longs for food, and it's called cravings! Many times, our bodies crave foods that are unhealthy for us. Our bodies crave salty things, such as potato chips, French fries, and pretzels. Do our bodies ever crave steamed broccoli without melted cheese?

Our bodies make seek satisfaction through food, but this satiation is often short-lived. A minute on the lips can be a lifetime on our hips. Is a minute of satisfaction worth the weight gain? Jesus satisfies. It is our joy and honor to live the life Jesus wants us to live. May we satisfy Him with our food choices. It will be great to hear our Lord say, *Well done, good and faithful servant; thou hast been faithful over a few things, I will make thee ruler over many things: enter thou into the joy of thy lord* (Matthew 25:23). Can I confidently choose the right foods for my plate and overall well-being, ensuring a healthy lifestyle? If not, let's work towards reaching that point.

When saying grace over a meal that is heavily laden with sugar, high fats, processed, high carbohydrates, and over the salt limit, I wonder what God is thinking. At times, guilt may overpower the person partaking in the meal as grace is spoken over the meal. Hopefully, this guilt allows one to recognize that those food choices do not bring health benefits to the body. Moderation is key in the eating of those types of foods. There is a difference between occasional indulgence and consistent consumption of such meals. How long do these meals truly satisfy our emotional and physical needs? Choose food wisely.

Oh Lord,

I find contentment in You alone, for You are the only one who can truly satisfy me. While on this journey, help me remember that only You have the power to satisfy my deepest needs. Please let my planned meals satisfy me until the next meal, so I won't crave more food until the next one. Lord, may I honor you with my food choices.
In Jesus' name,

Amen

Healthy Lifestyle Tip – Enhance the flavor of fish, salads, and vegetables by adding a refreshing touch of lemon juice after the cooking process.

SELF-CONTROL IN ALL THINGS
Day 78

Galatians 5:22-23 (NIV)
But the fruit of the Spirit is love, joy, peace, forbearance, kindness,
goodness, faithfulness, [23] gentleness and self-control. Against such
things there is no law.

What is self-control? Self-control is managing one's impulses and behavior. Lord, please help us with self-control. The Bible talks about taming and controlling our tongues in James 1:26, and today's scripture encompasses all the fruits of the Spirit. For many of us, if we exercised self-control with our food issues, we would not be in the predicament that we are in, possibly overweight or obese. Now, for some, certain medications have caused weight gain. For many of us, self-control in our eating habits has been a problem. My food coach's mother said that self-control is self-command.

Have you been to a food buffet? As you fill your plate at the buffet, keep your goals in mind and make mindful choices, that align

156

with your health journey. Remember the "whys" of your journey and refrain from impulse eating. Take the opportunity to enjoy the variety offered at the buffet while staying true to your healthy eating plan. It is not a sin to consume foods that aren't on your meal plan. The concern arises when we overindulge and eat in excess. Does my body really need eight different meats?

Why am I on this weight loss journey, and what is the motivation to stay on course? God said that self-control is a fruit of the spirit. The lack of self-control often results in impulsive behaviors and poor eating choices.

When posed with food choices that do not align with our food plan, exercise self-control. Should we possess all the fruits of the spirit? I think so. We need love, joy, peace, forbearance, kindness, goodness, faithfulness, gentleness, and self-control. Strive to master all the fruits of the spirit. Is self-control in your fruit bowl?

Dear Lord,

I humbly seek your guidance in cultivating self-control. Grant me the strength to overcome impulsive desires and unhealthy cravings. When my impulses and unhealthy cravings overpower me and temptations arise, empower me to exercise self-control. Thank you, Jesus, in advance. I am victorious.
In Jesus' name,

Amen

Healthy Lifestyle Tip – If large quantities of food are a problem, eat weighed and measured food portions. (The food scale can be your friend and helper.)

GIVE THANKS

Day 79

I Thessalonians 5:18
In every thing give thanks: for this is the will of God in Christ Jesus
concerning you.

Give thanks? Do we give thanks that we have a weight problem? Of course not. Give thanks to God that we have the mindset to make a change! Give thanks. We made a commitment to live a healthy lifestyle.

Thank you, God, for the food on today's food plan. Complaining about what's on the plate may kill a beautiful well-planned meal. Eat colorful, flavorful food cooked by you, a family member, or a personal chef that meets the approval of your eyes, but maintain your food plan. People eat with their eyes first. Need help to do this? Research quick and easy recipes from the internet, Instagram, and cookbooks that boost your skill set or stretch your skills.

Give thanks for every ounce and pound of excess weight that leaves the body. Losing 10 pounds every week is a great goal, but it is not a consistently realistic goal, even if you're on a television reality weight loss show. Strive to lose the excess weight, no matter what the number. Losing one to two pounds a week is something to be grateful for.

Grateful that I have food in my refrigerator. Thankful that I can eat three meals a day. No matter where you eat your meals, pray over every meal. Tell God thanks for the food that has been prepared and ready for consumption. Give thanks with a grateful heart. For this is the will of God in Christ Jesus! Let's be in His will. Give thanks! Yes, Lord!

Dear Lord,

I'm giving thanks to you for being on this journey. Enjoying healthy, colorful food with portion control is my desire and prayer. Thank you for the excess pounds that are gone and the future pounds leaving my body. Thank you, Lord, that I have the mind and commitment to live a healthy lifestyle. When the journey gets difficult, empower me to stay the course.
In Jesus' name,

Amen

Healthy Lifestyle Tip – Drink water instead of low or zero-calorie drinks.

TEMPTATION 3.0
Day 80

James 1:2-3 (NIV)
Consider it pure joy, my brothers and sisters, whenever you face trials
of many kinds, ³because you know that the testing of your faith
produces perseverance.

Quickly think of three foods that will tempt you to leave your healthy lifestyle, diet, or food plan. (Pause.) For some of us, the number went beyond three. Have you seen weight loss reality shows that place the contestants in a room by themselves with the foods that led them to obesity? This is a cruel temptation. Some contestants yield to the temptations. Others walk away without giving in to the temptation challenge. The pain that their bodies have endured because of overeating and the misuse of those foods is their reminder.

The temptation to consume high-calorie foods surrounds us, from parties to restaurants, bakeries, gas stations, and even supermarkets. Ask yourself, is this food option in alignment with my goals? Will this food item help me meet my goals? Avoid grocery shopping on an empty stomach, as it leads to impulsive purchases. Remember, temptation does not add weight to our bodies. Giving in and yielding to temptation can contribute to overall weight gain.

When unhealthy cravings arise, do not flirt with them. Run! Flee! Speak an affirmation or scripture to support your decision. We are not the first people who had trouble resisting food. Adam and Eve ate the forbidden fruit from the Tree of Good and Evil. There were so many other options for them to eat, but no! They wanted that piece of fruit. The Bible does not mention if Adam and Eve were even hungry! Their disobedience was a sin problem. They did not listen to God's directive, but they listened to Satan tell them that God did not mean what he said.

There are often other healthy options instead of eating poorly. But no! We want what we want when we want. And the food tastes good! If we are truly hungry, our resolve to eat healthily can quickly leave us.

Temptations will always be present, but we need God's strength to resist! Pray when temptation arises, join support groups, or call a friend who will encourage you. Have a plan in place for situations that bring on temptations. Set yourself up for success. Perseverance is key to staying on the weight loss journey. Missteps may happen. Push through. Do not quit. Persevere! Your health matters.

Dear Lord,

I desire to maintain a consistent commitment to healthy eating and living while resisting temptation. My aim is to remain steadfast on the right path. In Jesus' name, Amen

Healthy Lifestyle Tip – When your trigger foods and snacks are the joys of others at home or in the workplace, have a plan in place to handle temptation.

HOPE IN THE LORD
Day 81

Isaiah 40:31 (NIV)
But those who hope in the Lord will renew their strength. They will
soar on wings like eagles; they will run and not grow weary, they will
walk and not be faint.

In our scripture reference for today, different Bible versions use the words "hope," "trust," and "wait on the Lord" to find strength from Him. Do you have faith that weight loss and changing your eating habits are achievable? The data, reports, research, and testimonies of those who lost weight say it is. Consistently doing the work, making eating habit changes, and adding exercise ensures weight loss.

Eagles have great eyesight, and they see better than humans. Their great vision allows them to see what they want. When they soar, the eagle's wings spread out with confidence and strength as they rise into the sky. Isaiah the prophet was graphic in his description of flying like eagles in today's scripture reference.

Although we do not need exercise to lose weight, it is good for the health of the body. Walking and running are forms of exercise. However, Isaiah was speaking metaphorically.

God promised to renew our strength. I'm not sure how people lose excess weight without God's help. His power, strength, and wisdom give hope to His children. While on this weight loss journey, weariness can set in. Do not let this impede your progress. Rest in our heavenly Father. Continue to follow the steps of weight loss. Find new, healthy foods and recipes to encourage you.

Please remember, this journey is for a lifetime. If we go back to our old eating habits, the weight will quickly return. Commit to this lifestyle change and maintain your diligence as you guard against the weight that has left you. God promised to renew our strength for the journey, and God keeps His promises! Wait, hope, trust, and have faith in God to renew us with strength.

Dear Lord,

My faith, hope, trust, and patience are all rooted in you. I acknowledge that I cannot do this by myself. Without you, I am helpless, lost, and weak. My dependence is fully on you. Taking care of my temple is an enormous task for me, but I will do the work.
In Jesus' name,

Amen

Healthy Lifestyle Tip – Gaining weight is easier than losing it. Stay on the weight loss journey.

THE PLAN

Day 82

Jeremiah 29:11 (NIV)
For I know the plans I have for you," declares the LORD, "plans to
prosper you and not to harm you, plans to give you hope and a future.

There are so many food plans, diet plans, and exercise plans, and each of those plans does not work for everyone. However, there is an ultimate plan for each of us, God's plan for us. It is not God's plan for His children to be obese, be at risk, or suffer from diseases that are caused by being overweight. Are we bringing our bodies into alignment with His plan?

When you want to talk to Jesus, there are no phone numbers to memorize, no data rates applied, no roaming charges, no busy signals, and no dead cell phone tower zones. So, who are you going to call? Call on the Lord.

The Lord wants us to live a more abundant life. He wants us to prosper in all things. Let's live and prosper in a healthy body, which is why we are on this weight loss journey.

In previous devotionals, we emphasized the significance of establishing a well-defined food plan. Keep it at the forefront of your journey and make adjustments based on your lifestyle and your doctor's recommendations. Stay committed and adhere to the plan.

A plan gives us focus and direction. The plan guides the goals, objectives, and actions. So, what is your plan for healthy eating and/or weight loss?

The plan is to

.

Hear my prayer, Oh Lord. I am blessed that I can call on you in the morning, at noontime, in the evening, and at midnight. Twenty-four hours a day and seven days a week, I can call you. I am so grateful for the access to your throne. So glad you have plans for me.
In Jesus' name,

Amen

Healthy Lifestyle Tip – Daily write your food plan (menu) in a food journal, online journal or notes, or in a physical book.

THE JOURNEY
Day 83

I Corinthians 9:24 (NIV)
Do you not know that in a race all the runners run, but only one gets
the prize? Run in such a way as to get the prize.

In the Christian race, when we get to heaven, our prize is life eternal with Jesus in heaven. Our goal, our prize, and our joy is eternal life! In a race, there is a journey from the beginning to the finish line. There is always a beginning and an end. The length of a race varies. How long have you been on the weight loss journey? When did you begin? Have you met any of your weight loss goals?

Stay on the journey. Run the race. Slow and steady wins! Can you visualize yourself at the finish line? Are there obtainable, realistic goals and benchmarks along the way? Look at the list of goals you wrote on Day 10. There is a new body waiting for us as we eat healthy and make great food choices. Run well. In this race, you are the only runner. Your race, your pace. You can do it. The prize is a right-sized healthy body. Who determines that? Society? No! You,

166

your doctor, and the data results from your blood work and other assessments determine the health of your body.

On the lifestyle journey, the focus is eating healthy, with the prize being a healthy body. God is with us on this journey. He is with us the entire time, from the beginning to the end. There is a prize at the finish line, a healthy body. The benefits of a healthy body are many. Can you name them?

This is our journey. It's up to us! Finish strong. Go to the end. Stay on the healthy lifestyle journey. Your life matters.

Dear Lord,

I lift you up today. I thank you for all the help you have given me during this lifestyle change. As I have changed my bad eating habits, may I constantly remember that overeating and large portions are not beneficial for my body. Help me remain humble, despite the weight loss I've achieved. I honor and lift you up today for the discipline you have given me. Thank you, dear Father.
In Jesus' name,

Amen

Healthy Lifestyle Tip – For motivation, place, tape, or hang a former picture of you in your right-sized body in your bedroom, kitchen, or bathroom.

PERFECT PEACE

Day 84

Isaiah 26:3
Thou wilt keep him in perfect peace, whose mind is stayed on thee:
because he trusteth in thee.

Hopefully, there is peace of mind and a sense of peace in one's spirit, knowing that God is in control of our lives. Taking care of one's body through diet and exercise leads us onto the pathway to a healthy right-sized body. This healthy lifestyle may not rid us of all diseases, but it will help lower the risk of some weight-related ones.

Some people suffer from a lack of peace because of the troubles and burdens in their lives. Many worry about their health concerns, body image, and/or carrying around the extra weight. The lack of peace in our minds is a heavyweight. Some people have lost their minds due to major troubles, grief, and terrible situations, but our God gives us peace. Let's get a handle on our bad eating habits. Stress can also possibly hinder weight loss. Find ways to manage stress.

Take a walk, pray, remove yourselves if possible from stressful situations, or exercise.

If you are going through a terrible life event, God will grant you peace. His Word says so. We must keep our mind stayed on Him. This is not always easy because of the many variables and things happening around us. John 10:10A (NIV) states *The thief comes only to steal, and to kill, and destroy.* The devil wants to steal your joy and peace. Please do not give it to him. Go back to the Word of God. John 10:10B (NIV), "I have come that they might have life, and have it to the full." He will keep us in perfect peace. *You will keep me in perfect peace, those whose minds are steadfast, because they trust in you.* (Isaiah 26:3 NIV).

Oh Lord, our Lord,

I come before you today seeking peace in my current situation. You alone fully understand what I'm going through. Keeping my mind focused on you is my desire. Draw me nearer to you, Lord.

In Jesus' name,

Amen

Healthy Lifestyle Tip – Complete the last meal of the day 2 -3 hours before going to bed. Establish a cut-off time for eating (e.g., 6:30 PM, 7:00 PM, or 7:30 PM.)

LACK CONFIDENCE?

Day 85

Proverbs 3:26
For the Lord shall be thy confidence, and shall keep thy foot from being
taken.

D o you struggle with confidence in losing weight? You are
not alone. Countless individuals have faced setbacks on
their weight loss journeys. In fact, even prominent figures
in the Bible encountered moments of self-doubt in other areas. One
such example is Moses in the Old Testament, who lacked confidence.
However, God had a profound conversation with Moses, assuring
him of His presence and support. Empowered by this divine
encouragement, Moses walked a path of leadership with confidence
(Exodus 3:11 - 4:13). Just as Moses was empowered by divine
encouragement, we, too, can be inspired and strengthened by these
narratives to cultivate and nurture our confidence.

No one can demand that you stay on a healthy eating plan; it's a choice. You can cheat, lie, sneak foods that are not on your plan, and fool yourself, but the body will tell it all.

We all need confidence that we will continue this healthy lifestyle journey and be successful. Who gives us confidence? God does! If we let Him, God will see us through. God supports us as we resist temptation and craft our food menus. Keep going and do not quit.

Making excellent decisions has numerous benefits. If we walk in wellness, it can set us on the path toward an exceptional quality of life. Jesus will take all our burdens and cares about living in a body that is overweight or obese, and He will give us satisfaction, smiles, and the joy of living when we eat right and shed excess weight.

Commit to showing up for you, put in the effort to choose and eat the foods that are good for your body, eat the correct portions, and exercise to live a healthy lifestyle. The Lord is with you! Be confident in Him; continue this healthy lifestyle journey and be successful.

Dear Lord,

You are the light of life. You brighten the dark path. I am truly grateful for the confidence that you give me. I've got confidence! You will help me get to the finish line if I do not quit. I can do all things through Christ that strengthens me (Philippians 4:13). Thank you, Jesus. My confidence is in you.
In Jesus' name,

Amen and Amen

Healthy Lifestyle Tip – Consider adding weight training to your exercise regime. Newbies should start with light weights.

THE TRUTH

Day 86

John 8:32
And ye shall know the truth, and the truth shall make you free.

Know your numbers! For example, if the Body Mass Index (BMI), blood sugar, cholesterol levels, and blood pressure readings are high, lower your numbers with diet and exercise. Knowing the truth about one's health will help one strive to be healthier, and ignoring this information can be deadly. Listen, talk to, and obey your doctor!

Some people would rather believe a lie than the truth. When this is true, let the scales drop from our eyes and be open to the truth. Am I lying to myself? What will we do with the truth? What is the truth? Truth is, knowing that Jesus Christ is Lord and accepting Him into your heart for salvation gives us eternal life. Eating less, exercising 4-6 times a week, sleeping 7-9 hours a night, and daily drinking at least 6-8 eight-ounce cups of water will help us lose excess weight.

. . .

Dispelling Lies and Myths and Embracing The Truth

Lie 1: Extra calories per day do not affect our weight or bodies.

Truth: Excess calories not burned get stored as fat in our bodies, leading to weight gain.

Lie 2: A cup of steamed broccoli and a cup of multicolored jellybeans are equal in weight and nutrition.

Truth: While food can be equal in weight, they differ significantly in nutrition. Broccoli offers vital nutrients while jelly beans provide empty calories.

Myth 1: We need to exercise to lose weight.

Truth: Exercise is not mandatory for weight loss, but it plays a significant role in our overall health and well-being.

Myth 2: Don't believe the weight categories. I'm not obese, just pleasingly plump.

Truth: If our BMI falls into the obese category, specific risks for specific diseases may arise, even if we feel pleasingly plump.

Let us embrace the truth about our bodies and weight loss and make informed decisions to lead healthier lives. Let the truth set you free.

Dear Lord,

Knowing you as my Savior sets me free from the bondage of sin and death. I pray others may find and know the truth as I do. Lord, help me be intentional about living a healthy lifestyle. Please help me as I work towards having my health numbers at normal levels in order to take care of my temple. In Jesus' name, Amen.

Healthy Lifestyle Tip – Bites, licks, and tastes add up with caloric intake. Keep track of everything that goes into your mouth.

WHATSOEVER YE DO

Day 87

I Corinthians 10:31
Whether therefore ye eat, or drink, or whatsoever ye do, do all to the
glory of God.

Whatsoever ye eat or drink, do all to the glory of God. While saying grace over my food, I sometimes feel guilty because I know what is on my plate is not good for me. God knows this and so do I. Maybe if we recited today's scripture reference before eating, we would eat right. A written food plan for the day is a great deterrent to eating foods not good for us. Be mindful of what goes into your mouth. Unfortunately, there is no pill or liquid formula that will reduce the calories of a dish that was just eaten. Choose to eat right.

Let's take care of our bodies. Gluttony and binge eating do not glorify God. In fact, gluttony is a sin. (Proverbs 23:21) Remember, sugary drinks and alcoholic beverages can also add extra weight to

174

our bodies. Fruits and vegetables are necessary and beneficial for a healthy lifestyle.

Stay committed to the journey. The Word of God says to eat and drink to the glory of God. Drinking heavy-laden sugary soda is not a sin, but be mindful of the huge amounts of sugar in each can or bottle, which can affect our health and the health of our children. Read the nutrition label on sugary drinks.

Having a juicy ribeye steak for dinner is not a sin. Having a one-pound ribeye, which is at least 3 or 4 servings, is something to reconsider. Daily food decisions require thoughtful actions. Am I eating this meal and/or the amount of food to the glory of God? Will this meal help me reach my goal weight and my right-sized body?

After reciting our verse today, can we really eat a whole 13-inch pizza and glorify God if we are on a weight loss program? (One medium 13-inch cheese pizza is about 1223 calories.) Lord, give us restraint when choosing our food and portions.

Dear Lord,

I want to eat and drink to the glory of God. Please help me be mindful of what goes into my mouth, knowing that gluttony does not glorify you. Lord, I pray for restraint when faced with tempting foods that may hinder my progress. May I seek Your strength to make healthy choices. This is my hope and prayer.

In Your Name, I pray,
Amen

Healthy Lifestyle Tip – Read drink labels for sugar content, nutritional value, and calories. Reduce and/or limit sugary drinks. If you can, totally stop drinking heavy-laden sugary sodas.

REJOICE IN THE DANCE
Day 88

Jeremiah 31:13
Then shall the virgin rejoice in the dance, both young men and old
together: for I will turn their mourning into joy, and will comfort them,
and make them rejoice from their sorrow.

There are so many ways to rejoice. We rejoice in praise to God in the singing of songs, the playing of instruments, the clapping of hands, and the movement of dance. In Psalm 150, David directs us on how to praise the Lord. Praise the Lord with the trumpet, psaltery, harp, timbrel, stringed instruments, organs, loud cymbals, high-sounding cymbals, and dance. Can you imagine this beautiful sound and the picturesque setting of rejoicing?

Use movement and dance to help you get to your healthy right-sized weight and body. When the ark of the Lord was brought to the city of David, David danced before the Lord (2 Samuel 6:12-14). David danced to rejoice before the Lord. According to Exodus 15:20, *And Miriam the prophetess, the sister of Aaron, took a timbrel in her hand; and all the women went out after her with timbrels and with dances.* The Bible said dancing turned the virgin's heart from sadness into joy (Jeremiah 31:13).

Dance, dance, dance! Move your body. Movement is medicine for the body. Salsa, Zumba, and aerobic dancing, which are fast-moving dances, help burn calories. Praise the Lord in the dance while burning calories and exercising your body. Enjoy dancing and have fun! Many of us may need to and should stretch and warm up our bones and ligaments before dancing for Jesus. Then dance. Dance, O ye people!

Dear Lord,

May my feet and my two steps give you praise. I am not sure which dance steps David had in the Old Testament, but may my dance steps today be for your glory. As I move, may I exercise my heart and body. In all that I do, I want to glorify you.
In Jesus' name,

Amen

Healthy Lifestyle Tip – Exercise to a dance video, YouTube dance video, exercise tape, or take a dance class.

A JOYFUL HEART

Day 89

Proverbs 17:22 (ESV)
*A joyful heart is the health of the body, but a depressed spirit dries up
the bones.*

The human heart is a vessel that pumps 1.5 gallons of blood to different parts of the body every minute, which is about 2000 gallons a day. Each day, our hearts beat over 100,000 times per day. [1] We want to live in a healthy body, which includes a healthy heart.

A healthy heart is necessary for healthy living. Today's scripture in the NIV says *A joyful heart is like good medicine.* Saints of God, this type of medicine needs no prescription from the doctor! Joy is one of the fruits of the spirit. Being grateful, obedient to the Lord, spending time in His presence and His Word, being a doer of the Word, and confessing sin cultivates a joyful heart. Jesus gives us joy and brightens our day, no matter what size we are.

Good health in your body, soul, and mind is exhilarating. Eat 4-5 servings of fresh vegetables and fruit each day, drink 6-8 eight-ounce cups of water, sleep 7-9 hours of sleep every night, and complete aerobic exercise 4-5 days a week for at least 30 minutes. Healthy living is for everyone, no matter the condition of our bodies.

Losing excess weight from our bodies through diet, exercise, and mindful eating brings joy to our bodies. Our bodies cannot speak, but they react and respond to what we put in them. Be kind to your heart and body. Many people know the right way to healthy eating by listening to teachers and doctors, reading articles and pamphlets, and the testimonies of family, friends, and others. Knowing the path to healthy eating is great, but be doers of the knowledge given to us about eating right.

Sad or depressed about your weight or the condition of your body? Start with small changes to your diet. Then continually add more healthy eating habits to your lifestyle. When the weight drops from the body, we lighten a physical burden. Let it go with joy in your heart. Strive to release the excess weight with God's help and healthy eating. It's not worth the weight. Come on! Bring on the joy! Joy for the journey!

Dear Lord,

A joyful, grateful heart is my prayer today. I want a healthy heart pumping in my body as I eat healthily and exercise.
In Jesus' name,

Amen

Healthy Lifestyle Tip – Be grateful for the journey!

RECOMMIT

Day 90

Proverbs 16:3 (NIV)
Commit to the Lord whatever you do, and he will establish your plans.

So how is the journey of healthy eating progressing? Today, no matter what day you are on, or the highs and lows of your weight loss journey, recommit to the journey. Do not give up. Show up every day, stick to the plan, and be consistent. While it is acceptable to indulge or "cheat" in moderation occasionally, it is important to plan for those days. Stay committed to the healthy lifestyle plan, weight loss plan, or diet that you started. If modifications are needed, make those adjustments.

The Lord cares about your hopes, goals, and dreams for your life and health. Continue to ask Him for guidance and help while on this lifetime journey. If you give up or stop the healthy eating lifestyle or go back to old bad eating habits, previous loss of weight will definitely come back, maybe even with more pounds. The fat cells will be re-energized and the body will grow. Let the fat cells stay dormant in your body! Do not wake them up!

As you know by now, a weight loss plan will work if we put in the effort. Give all your cares, meals and exercise plans, and problems to the Lord. Decide on your level of commitment to living a healthy lifestyle. Are you ready to do the work? Our commitment will determine our success. *Commit your way to the LORD, trust in Him, and He will do this* (Psalm 37:5 ESV). It is His desire for us to be in a relationship with Him in all things. He cares!

Healthy eating and weight loss are achievable. When we are weak, He is strong. Keep going! Until we meet again with less of you, go with God, and be devoted to a healthy lifestyle.

Dear Lord,

Today, I recommit to my weight loss program called_____.
In Jesus' name, Amen.

Or

Dear Lord,
Today, I recommit to remaining on a healthy lifestyle, which entails

--.

I want to honor you with my eating habits and in my temple. When I am weak, I am strong. I can do all things through you, which strengthens me. In Jesus' name, Amen.

Healthy Lifestyle Tip – Recommit to staying on the healthy lifestyle journey.

Before weight loss———————————————After Weight loss

Podcast Cover Art for "Grace Notes: Devotions at the Piano with Marlene"

I am still on my journey of healthy eating. The excess weight is leaving my body. Thank you, Lord, for being with me on the journey.

Marlene's Weight Loss Food Plan

Breakfast

- 2 eggs or 2 oz of cheese or 6-8 oz of low-fat plain Greek yogurt or 4 oz of cottage cheese
- 1 oz 100% whole grain old-fashioned or 5-minute quick oats (not the packets) or 1 oz of shredded wheat (not frosted)
- 6 oz fruit – medium size fruit or slices

Lunch

- 4 oz protein, meat or fish or 2 oz of legumes or beans or 2 eggs or 2 oz of cheese or 6-8 oz of low-fat plain Greek yogurt
- 6 oz of cooked vegetables
- 8 oz salad
- 6 oz fruit – medium fruit or slices
- 1 tablespoon extra-virgin olive oil, salad dressing, or mayonnaise

Dinner

- 4 oz protein, meat or fish, or 2 oz of legumes or beans or 2 eggs or 2 oz of cheese or 6-8 oz of low-fat plain Greek yogurt
- 6 oz of cooked vegetables
- 8 oz salad
- 1 tablespoon extra-virgin olive oil, salad dressing, or mayonnaise

Choose any foods to meet the above requirements.

Please note:

No white refined all-purpose flour or white processed sugar is in my personal food plan. (Occasionally, a "cheat" day is permitted. Plan ahead.)

A Cuisinart Air Fryer is used to substitute for deep-fried foods.

I use PAM or Bertolli Extra Olive Oil Spray, a zero-calorie cooking spray, to coat my pan when sautéing or grilling.

I use All-Clad, Le Creuset, and cast-iron cookware. Quality cookware makes a difference in cooking.

Change the protein for each meal of the day.

I substitute white all-purpose flour for oat flour, red lentil flour, almond flour, and chickpea flour products.

Occasionally, I:

- save my "fat" (olive oil or dressing) from lunch and add it to the dinner plan. (1 ounce total for dinner and for the day)
- make a smoothie with yogurt and fruit, along with 3 oz of Unsweetened Almond Milk
- add 1 or 2 Ezekiel slices of bread, which contain no refined white flour or sugar

- add my fruit to the cooked oatmeal
- place 2 sunny-side, poached, or hard-boiled eggs on top of my cooked oatmeal or avocado toast
- add 1-2 oz of vegetables to my breakfast menu to make an omelet.

Exercise Plan

- Walk 5-6 times a week for one hour to 80 minutes.
- Spin on an exercise bike for 45 minutes
- Swim for 30-45 minutes, occasionally at the gym

Marlene's Lemon- Mustard Vinaigrette
(1 serving)

- Slice one lemon in half.
- Remove the seeds.
- Squeeze the juice of both halves into a bowl.
- Add ½ teaspoon of Dijon mustard.
- Salt and pepper to taste.
- Stir/whisk all ingredients until blended.

Options

- Add 1 tablespoon of extra-virgin olive oil to the above ingredients.
- Add 1 tablespoon of white balsamic vinegar to the above ingredients.

(These healthy options will increase the calorie amount, but will add great flavor.)

Healthy Lifestyle Tips Index

Day 1 - Portion control for each food group on your plate.

Day 2 - Let sleeping and shrunken fat cells stay shrunken.

Day 3 - Write the food plan in a food journal.

Day 4 - Walk for at least 30 minutes a day 5 days a week. If you are on a walking journey, build up to 30 minutes a day.

Day 5 - Replace unhealthy eating habits with healthy ones.

Day 6 - Reduce at least 5-15 percent of the excess weight.

Day 7 - Eliminate refined sugar and processed carbohydrates.

Day 8 - Live a daily life of consistent healthy eating.

Day 9 - Eat a small snack or meal before attending a food event.

Day 10 - Set specific, measurable, achievable, relevant, and time-bound goals. Write them down.

Day 11 - Eliminate or reduce sugary drinks from your diet.

Day 12 - Place a scripture that encourages weight loss on the refrigerator or somewhere in the kitchen.

Day 13 - Make small changes to your diet to achieve healthy living and potential weight loss.

Day 14 - Praise the Lord for big and small wins in weight loss. Celebrate with non-food rewards!

Day 15 - Make a poster about the "Whys" of your weight loss journey.

Day 16 - Strive for 7-9 hours of sleep each night.

Day 17 - Visualize your success in your right-sized body.

Day 18 - Keep a food diary or journal of your health and weight loss numbers, daily food plans, and comments.

Day 19 - Try an unfamiliar fruit.

Day 20 - Give a new easy recipe a try.

Day 21 - Be mindful of your daily intake of salt in your diet.

Day 22 - Cook and eat at home! Limit restaurant eating.

Day 23 - Post before and now pictures in the bathroom.

Day 24 - Do not stress over having to lose 50 pounds. Focus on one day at a time.

Day 25 - Drink green tea without refined sugar.

Day 26 - Form a habit of sitting down at the table while eating.

Day 27 - Be consistent with exercise and healthy eating.

Day 28 - Stress can hinder weight loss. Let it go!

Day 29 - Speak an affirmation out loud.

Day 30 - Pray first and ask God for strength to stick with your lifestyle change.

Day 31 - Try the Daniel fast for spiritual renewal.

Day 32 - Refrain from eating between meals except for planned snacks.

Day 33 - Eat at least 2 servings a day of fruit.

Day 34 - Be the queen or king, the ruler/manager of your temple. Make the right food choices.

Day 35 - Eliminate refined sugar from your diet. Replace refined sugar with honey, agave, or fruit purees.

Day 36 - Stay hydrated and infuse water with cucumbers, lemons, or limes.

Day 37 - Never shop at the supermarket when hungry.

Day 38 - Start your day with breakfast.

Day 39 - Celebrate every win, big or small.

Day 40 - Keep trigger foods out of sight.

Day 41 - Do not let food pushers sway you to eat foods not on your plan.

Day 42 - Instead of salt, flavor foods with fresh herbs, spices, and dried herbs.

Day 43 - Eat what you love in moderation with self-control and a pre-determined food portion. Be careful.

Day 44 - Eat three meals every day. Do not skip meals.

Day 45 - Hydrate the body. Drink at least 6-8 eight-ounce glasses of water a day.

Day 46 - Review your healthy eating lifestyle plan. Are changes or modifications needed?

Day 47 - Encourage yourself with words of affirmation.

Day 48 - Add a meatless or plant-based meal this week.

Day 49 - If you mess up, binge, go off the plan, or fall off the wagon, regroup, forgive yourself, and get back on track.

Day 50 - Keep a daily log, journal, or progress chart of weight, exercises, and personal thoughts for the day.

Day 51 - Let every diner at the table finish their own food.

Day 52 - Meal prepping ahead of scheduled meals makes cooking meals easier during the week.

Day 53 - Eat high-fiber snacks, which keep you full.

Day 54 - Incorporate protein into your three main meals.

Day 55 - Consider having an accountability partner, coach, or mentor during your weight loss, healthy living journey.

Day 56 - Read the food labels. Know the calories and nutritional breakdown of your food.

Day 57 - Choose fresh fruit and vegetables. Farm to Table.

Day 58 - Refrain from drinking your calories.

Day 59 - Eliminate saturated and trans fats (bad fats) from your food plan. Choose healthy fats (good fats).

Day 60 - Eliminate white refined all-purpose flour.

Day 61 - Make at least 2-3 changes in your bad eating habits.

Day 62 - Start your day early. Read your Bible, exercise, and eat breakfast.

Day 63 - Try the Daniel Fast for one meal per week or for an entire month to three months.

Day 64 - Is your body screaming for fiber and nutritious food? Try an unfamiliar vegetable or fruit.

Day 65 - Avoid processed foods and fast-food restaurants.

Day 66 - The overeating of vegetables, fruits, and lean proteins can create excess weight in our bodies. Portion control is key.

Day 67 - Self-care! Self-care might reduce stress in one's life or give a break from it. Take care of yourself!

Day 68 - For emergencies, keep healthy snacks at home, work, or in your car.

Day 69 - Make a healthy salad dressing or vinaigrette.

Day 70 - Stay on this journey! Take one meal at a time.

Day 71 - Mindful eating at all meals! Be mindful and present while eating a meal. Know what's going in your mouth.

Day 72 - As much as possible, eat home-cooked meals with controlled portions.

Day 73 - Seek, pray, and ask God for help with making the right choices for healthy eating. Then use it!

Day 74 - Since we eat with our eyes first, cook flavorful, healthy meals with ingredients of many colors on the plate.

Day 75 - Choose to start your day with a healthy breakfast.

Day 76 - Read, write, meditate, speak, and memorize those verses that will encourage you on this journey.

Day 77 - Add a squeeze of lemon after the cooking process to brighten fish, salads, and vegetables.

Day 78 - Eat weighed and measured food portions.

Day 79 - Drink water instead of low or zero-calorie drinks.

Day 80 - When your trigger foods and snacks are the joys of others at home or in the workplace, have a plan in place to handle temptation.

Day 81 - Gaining weight is easier than losing it.

Day 82 - Daily write your food plan (menu) in a food journal, online journal, or physical book.

Day 83 - For motivation, place or hang a former picture of you in your right-sized body in your bedroom, kitchen, or bathroom.

Day 84 - Finish the last meal 2 -3 hours before bedtime.

Day 85 - Consider adding weight training to your exercise regime. Newbies should start with light weights.

Day 86 - Bites, licks, and tastes add up with caloric intake.

Day 87 - Read the drink labels for sugar content, nutritional value, and calories.

Day 88 - Exercise to a dance video, YouTube dance video, exercise tape, or take a dance class.

Day 89 - Be grateful for the journey!

Day 90 - Recommit to staying on the healthy lifestyle journey.

Sample Mealtime Prayers

Dear Lord,
Bless this food, O Lord, I pray. May the components of this meal nourish me and give me strength. Thank you, Lord. In Jesus' name, Amen.

Dear Lord,
Thank you for the food on my plate. May it nourish me and keep me full until the next meal. Please help me continue to eat healthily. In Jesus' name, Amen.

Dear Lord,
Thank you, Lord, for the food that has been prepared for me. May I honor and glorify you as I eat this meal. May I enjoy it, and may it spur me on to continuous healthy eating. In Jesus' name, Amen.

Invitation to Salvation

The Plan of Salvation

I f you have read these devotionals but never repented of your sins and asked Christ to save you, you are in need of a Savior. Please consider repenting of your sins, and asking Jesus Christ to save you today. The steps are as easy as A, B, C.

Admit and Repent - Admit you have sinned against GOD and repent of your sins.

What is "sin?"

- Mark 7:21-23 – *For from within, out of the heart of men, proceed evil thoughts, adulteries, fornications, murders, thefts, covetousness, wickedness, deceit, lewdness, an evil eye, blasphemy, pride, foolishness. All these evil things come from within and defile a man.*
- James 4:17 – *Therefore, to him who knows to do good and does not do it, to him it is sin.*

What is "Admit and repent?"

- Psalm 51:3-4a – *For I acknowledge my transgressions, and my sin is always before me. Against You, You only, have I sinned, and done this evil in Your sight.*
- John 8:11b – *And Jesus said to her, Neither do I condemn you; go and sin no more.*

Believe and Receive – Believe what the Bible teaches about the Penalty of Sin; that Christ paid the penalty for your sin by His death on the cross, His burial, and His physical resurrection. Receive the gift of His payment in your place.

What is the "Penalty for sin?"

- Ezekiel 18:4 – *Behold, all souls are Mine; The soul of the father as well as the soul of the son is Mine; The soul who sins shall die.*
- Romans 6:23 – *For the wages of sin is death, but the gift of God is eternal life in Christ Jesus our Lord.*
- Hebrews 9:27 – *And as it is appointed for men to die once, but after this the judgment.*
- Revelation 20:12-15 – *And I saw the dead, small and great, standing before God, and books were opened. And another book was opened, which is the Book of Life. And the dead were judged according to their works, by the things, which were written in the books... Then Death and Hades were cast into the lake of fire. This is the second death. And anyone not found written in the Book of Life was cast into the lake of fire.*

What is "His death on the cross, His burial, and His physical resurrection?"

- 1 Corinthians 15:3-5 – *For I delivered to you first of all that which I also received: that Christ died for our sins according to the Scriptures, and that He was buried, and that He rose again the third day according to the Scriptures, and that He was seen by Cephas, then by the twelve.*

- Luke 24:39-40 (NKJV) – *Behold My hands and My feet, that it is I Myself. Handle Me and see, for a spirit does not have flesh and bones as you see I have. When He had said this, He showed them His hands and His feet.*

Call and Declare/Confess - Call on the Lord Jesus Christ to save you and declare publicly that He is your Lord and Master.

- Romans 10:13 – *For whoever calls on the name of the Lord shall be saved.*
- Romans 10:9, 10 - *If you confess with your mouth the Lord Jesus and believe in your heart that God has raised Him from the dead, you will be saved. For with the heart one believes unto righteousness, and with the mouth confession is made unto salvation.*

If you sincerely repent of your sins and believe what the Bible teaches about the penalty of sin (that you want to escape), and Jesus Christ's payment for your sins, by His death on the cross, burial, and resurrection from the dead; if you want Jesus Christ to save you, say the following prayer (or equivalent in your own words):

Repentant Sinner's Prayer for Salvation

Dear Lord Jesus Christ,

I admit my sins of thought, word, and deed. I admit that I have sinned against You and done evil in Your sight. I am sorry for my sins and have decided to turn away from them. Thank You for dying on the cross to pay the penalty for my sin. Please save me. Please forgive me for all my sins. Please come into my heart and take over as Lord of my life. I trust your promise that I will be saved if I call on your Name. Thank You for saving my soul today!
Amen.

If you prayed the prayer above (or equivalent in your own words), you have been born again, into God's Family. You are a child of God. What next?

1. Tell someone else, as soon as possible, about your decision and the action you took.
2. God wants you to be sure of the following five things:
3. Your salvation. 1 John 5:11-13
4. Your sins have been forgiven and will be forgiven if you stumble. 1 John 1:9
5. You can have victory over temptation. 1 Corinthians 10:13
6. Your prayers will be answered as you follow God's conditions. John 16:24
7. God will guide all your decisions. Proverbs 3:5,6
8. Get a Bible and read it daily (at least one chapter). Start with the New Testament (Matthew–Revelation), then the Old Testament (Genesis–Malachi).
9. Find fellowship and be active in a Bible-believing, Bible-practicing church.

ABOUT THE AUTHOR

Marlene Jenkins Cooper is the author of four books, *While in the Valley: Walking With God Through Divorce, Grace Notes: Five-Minute Inspirational Devotionals for the Church Choir, Musicians, and Friends of Music, Life 101: Money Management and Adulting Made Simple,* which won a 2021 Finalist award from American Writing Awards, and her latest release, *It's Not Worth The Weight: A 90-Day Weight Loss Devotional.*

Marlene Jenkins Cooper is an actively engaged member of Enon Tabernacle Baptist Church. She participates in various ministries, including music, youth scholarship, counseling, and serving as a devotionalist on the prayer line ministry. As the host of the podcast *Grace Notes: Devotion at the Piano with Marlene,* she shares her spiritual insights based on scripture with sacred music.

Having retired from the School District of Philadelphia, Marlene holds an illustrious career spanning thirty-four years. She began as a general vocal music teacher and later embraced the role of a computer specialist/teacher. She has received recognition from various organizations for her passionate teaching style and commitment to education.

Ms. Cooper holds music education degrees from Temple University and The King's College. Additionally, she pursued further graduate studies in computer technology at Temple University. She is the parent of two adult children and a loving grandmother to one granddaughter.

In addition to writing, Ms. Cooper enjoys a diverse range of activities, including reading, traveling, cooking, swimming, and playing tennis. Marlene Cooper's greatest desire is to lead more people into the Kingdom of God and encourage people to live victorious Christian lives.

DEVOTIONAL THEME INDEX

A Joyful Heart................................178............................ Day 89

A Testimony..................................136............................ Day 68

A Transformation.........................46............................. Day 23

Abide in Me..................................12.............................Day 6

All Things Possible......................116...........................Day 58

Be Strong in the Lord..................26............................Day 13

Cast Your Cares...........................44............................Day 22

Changed Bodies..........................14............................Day 7

Confidence in Him.......................78............................Day 39

Consistency is Key! ....64............................Day 32

Covet Not....................................84............................Day 42

Discipline.....................................18............................Day 9

Discouraged.................................140...........................Day 70

Don't Get Weary ....60............................Day 30

Drop the Burdens.........................24............................Day 12

Eat the Fruit!................................66............................Day 33

Encourage Yourself.......................94............................Day 47

Follow The Plan............................54............................Day 27

Marlene Jenkins Cooper

Freedom in Christ.............68.................Day 34
Friends on the Journey.............110.................Day 55
Fuel for the Body.............58.................Day 29
Give Thanks.............158.................Day 79
God, the Supplier.............148.................Day 74
God's Masterpiece.............88.................Day 44
Hallelujah!.............28.................Day 14
Having the Mind of Christ.............152.................Day 76
Heals All My Diseases.............102.................Day 51
Hope in the Lord.............162.................Day 81
Humble Me.............118.................Day 59
I See You.............134.................Day 67
I Will Restore.............138.................Day 69
In The Morning.............104.................Day 52
Is Anything Too Hard?.............146.................Day 73
Is Life More Than Food?.............130.................Day 65
Is This Food For Me?.............112.................Day 56
Jesus, The Chef.............150.................Day 75
Know Your Numbers.............36.................Day 18
Lack Confidence?.............170.................Day 85
Lack Wisdom?.............100.................Day 50
Lift Up Your Hands.............40.................Day 20
Living Water.............90.................Day 45
Love, Love, L-O-V-E.............86.................Day 43
More Than a Conqueror.............34.................Day 17
My Commitment.............92.................Day 46
My Help.............70.................Day 35
My Hope.............142.................Day 71
My New Body.............124.................Day 62
My Words Have Power.............144.................Day 72
New Mercies Are Mine.............114.................Day 57
One Day At A Time.............48.................Day 24
Our Refuge and Strength.............82.................Day 41

Our Temple................................4................................Day 2

Perfect Peace............................168............................Day 84

Prayer and Fasting ....62..............................Day 31

Prosper in Health.......................16..............................Day 8

Recommitment..........................180............................Day 90

Rejoice in the Dance...................176............................Day 88

Renewing Your Mind..................10..............................Day 5

Rest in the Lord..........................32..............................Day 16

Salt The Earth............................42..............................Day 21

Satisfy Him................................154............................Day 77

Self-Control In All Things...........156............................Day 78

Self-Love...................................108............................Day 54

Temptation 2.0..........................80..............................Day 40

Temptation 3.0..........................160............................Day 80

Temptations Arise.......................22..............................Day 11

That's Love................................128............................Day 64

The Blood..................................96..............................Day 48

The Desires of the Flesh..............132............................Day 66

The Flesh Speaks........................74..............................Day 37

The Food Test............................126............................Day 63

The Future Me...........................56..............................Day 28

The Goals..................................20..............................Day 10

The Journey...............................166............................Day 83

The Joy Thief ....72..............................Day 36

The Lust of the Eye....................52..............................Day 26

The Plan....................................164............................Day 82

The Requirements......................106............................Day 53

The Truth..................................172............................Day 86

This Day....................................76..............................Day 38

Victory is Mine!.........................120............................Day 60

Walk with Jesus.........................8................................Day 4

Weary?......................................50..............................Day 25

What is Your Name?...................38..............................Day 19

Whatsoever Ye Do........................174..Day 87

When I am Weak..........................98..Day 49

Why?..30...Day 15

Without Murmuring and Complaining...122............................Day 61

Write it Down....................................6...Day 3

Yes, I Can..2...Day 1

DEVOTIONAL SCRIPTURE INDEX

Old Testament

Joshua 1:9 NIV - page 94

II Samuel 17:29 ESV - page 58

Psalms 5:3 - page 104
    16:3 - page 54
    17:22 ESV - page 178
    31:24 - page 142
    37:4 ESV - page 20
    37:5 page 96
    46:1 - page 82
    55:22 - page 24
    91:16 - page 154
    103:3 NIV - page 102
    118:24 - page 76
    119:31 ESV - page 134
    121:1-2 - page 70

Psalms 139:14 ESV- page 108

Proverbs 3:26 - page 170
16:3 NIV - pages 54 & 180
17:22 ESV - page 178
18:21 NIV- page 144
29:18 - page 56

Isaiah 26:3 - page 168
40:31 NIV - page 162

Jeremiah 29:11 NIV - page 164
30:17 NIV - page 138
31:13 - page 176
32:27 - page 146

Lamentations 3:22-23 - page 114
3:41 - page 40

Daniel 1:15 - page 126

Habakkuk 2:2 ESV - page 6

Haggai 2:19 - page 66

* * *

New Testament

Matthew 4:2-3 ESV- page 80
5:13 - page 42
6:25 NIV - page 130
6:33 - page 8

Matthew 6:34 NIV - page 48
   11:28-30 - page 32
   19:26 NIV - page 116
   26:41 NIV - page 74

Mark 5:28 - page 36
   9:29 - page 62

Luke 21:13 - page 136

John 3:16 - page 86
   6:35 - page 90
   8:32 - page 172
   10:10 ESV - page 72
   14:2-3 - page 106
   14:27 - page 140
   15:5 NJKV - page 12
   21:9, 12-13 NIV - page 150

Romans
   5:8 NKJV - page 128
   8:37 - page 34
   12:2 - page 46

I Corinthians
   2:16 NIV - page 152
   3:16-17 - page 4
   6:12 ESV - page 112
   2:16 NIV - page 152
   6:19-20 - page 30
   9:24 NIV - page 166
   10:13 - page 22
   10:31 - page 174

I Corinthians 15:57 NIV- page 120
15:58 NIV - page 64

II Corinthians 5:17 - page 124
5:21 - page 38
12:10 - page 98
12:11 NIV - page 134

Galatians 5:1 - page 68
5:16 ESV - page 132
5:22-23 NIV - page 156
6:9 NIV - page 60

Ephesians 4:23 - page 10
2:10 ESV- page 88
6:10 NIV - page 26

Philippians 2:14 - page 122
3:20-21 NIV- page 14
4:13 NIV- page 2
4:19 - page 148

I Thessalonians 5:11 - page 110
5:18 - page 158

II Thessalonians 3:13 - page 50

II Timothy 1:7 ESV - page 18

Hebrews 13:5 - page 84

James 1:2-3 NIV - page 160
1:5 - page 100

James 4:10 - page 118

I Peter 5:7 - page 44

I John 1:7 - page 96
     2:16 - page 52
     5:14 - page 78

III John 1:2 ESV - page 16

Revelation 19:1 - page 28

ENDNOTES

YES, I CAN

1. https://www.healthline.com/health/obesity-facts. (Accessed October 26, 2022.)

WALK WITH JESUS

1. Dutta, Sanchari Sinha. "Why You Should Exercise in the Morning". News-Medical. https://www.news-medical.net/health/Why-You-Should-Exercise-in-the-Morning.aspx. (Accessed May 18, 2023.)

ABIDE IN ME

1. https://www.truthaboutweight.com/understanding-excess-weight.html? (Accessed June 5, 2022.)

THE GOALS

1. "SMART Goal-Definition, Guide, and Importance of Goal Setting", n.d., accessed September 7, 2020, https://coroporatefinanceinstitiute.com/resources/knowledge/other/smart-goal/

FOLLOW THE PLAN

1. https://www.collinsdictionary.com/us/dictionary/english/diet-regime/ (Accessed August 13, 2022.)

EAT THE FRUIT

1. Lee SH, Moore LV, Park S, Harris DM, Blanck HM. Adults Meeting Fruit and Vegetable Intake Recommendations — United States, 2019. MMWR Morb Mortal Wkly Rep 2022;71:1–9. DOI: http://dx.doi.org/10.15585/mmwr.mm7101a1. (Accessed July 17, 2023)

Marlene Jenkins Cooper

COVET NOT!

1. https://www.smithsonianmag.com/innovation/the-seesawing-history-of-fad-diets-180981586/ (Accessed May 24, 2023).

THE REQUIREMENT

1. The Invitation to Salvation and the Sinner's Prayer begins on page 192.

IS THIS FOOD FOR ME?

1. https://www.livestrong.com/article/182971-south-philly-cheese-steak-nutritional-information/ (Accessed May 12, 2022)

WITHOUT MURMURINGS and COMPLAINING

1. "Murmur - WordReference.com Dictionary of English." *Www.wordreference.com*, www.wordreference.com/definition/murmur. (Accessed June 28, 2023.)

A JOYFUL HEART

1. https://www.templehealth.org/about/blog/10-interesting-heart-facts-you-may-not-know. (Accessed April 15, 2023.)

AFTERWORD

Dear Friend,

I pray you may enjoy good health and that all may go well with you,
as you are on your weight loss journey.
Live a healthy, active lifestyle!
Bid farewell to excess weight!
Find strength in Jesus as you stay on the path!
Stay committed to the journey!

Hebrews 13:20-21 ESV
*Now may the God of peace who brought again from the dead our Lord
Jesus, the great shepherd of the sheep, by the blood of the eternal
covenant, [21]equip you with everything good that you may do his will,
working in us that which is pleasing in his sight, through Jesus Christ,
to whom be glory forever and ever. Amen.*

Blessings.

Marlene Jenkins Cooper

FEEDBACK and SUPPORT

I appreciate your purchase and taking the time to read my book. Your support means a lot to me, and I genuinely hope you found it valuable. If you enjoyed it, I kindly request you to consider sharing it with your loved ones and leaving an online review on Amazon, Goodreads, and/or your favorite book website. If you'd like to leave a review, please visit *It's Not Worth the Weight* on Amazon and Goodreads. Thank you once again!

Steps to leaving a review on Amazon.

1. Go to Amazon.com and log into your account.

2. Look for the book ***It's Not Worth the Weight*** at https://a.co/d/hzDVNdK

3. Click on the book's title and go to its product page.

4. Scroll down to the "Customer Review" section of the page.

5. Give a rating (out of 5 stars) and/or write a review in the text box provided.

Website - Marlenejenkinscooper.com

Email - Marlenejenkinscooper@gmail.com

Facebook—https://www.facebook.com/AuthorMarleneJenkinsCooper/

Also by Marlene Jenkins Cooper

Books

While In the Valley: Walking With God Through Divorce

Grace Notes: Five-Minute Inspirational Devotionals for the Church Choir, Musicians, and Friends of Music

Life 101: Money Management and Adulting Made Simple

QR code For All Books by Marlene Jenkins Cooper

Podcast - Grace Notes: Devotions at the Piano with Marlene